FOREWORD

The Programme centres on road and road transport research, while taking into account the impacts of intermodal aspects on the road transport system as a whole. It is geared towards a technico-economic approach to solving key road transport issues identified by Member countries. The Programme has two main fields of activity:

-- The international co-operation in road and road transport research to provide scientific support for decisions by Member governments and international governmental organisations, and to assess future strategies concerning roads and road transport problems and the priority policy concerns of Member countries;

-- The information and documentation programme (IRRD -- International Road Research Documentation), a co-operative scheme that provides a mechanism for the systematic world-wide exchange of information on scientific literature and current research programmes.

The scientific and technical activities concern:

-- The assessment of urban and inter-urban road transport strategies;

-- The development and management of road traffic control and driver communication systems to enhance network efficiency and quality of service;

-- The formulation and evaluation of integrated road and traffic safety programmes;

-- The construction, preservation and rehabilitation of road infrastructure.

-- The maintenance management of road infrastructure and the evaluation of traffic safety measures and strategies in developing countries.

ABSTRACT

IRRD No. 821249

The objectives of the study, supported by thirteen Member countries and the International Road Federation, were to review traffic operations at work zones assessing safety, traffic flow and economic impacts. Chapter I presents the current situation pointing out the need for improving the overall management of road works in a way which is both satisfactory to road users and economically acceptable. Chapter II gives an assessment of safety issues at work zones including the interpretation of traffic accident data. Chapter III discusses traffic analysis and cost evaluation techniques. It reviews the general application of traffic data, the cost evaluation elements and models with special emphasis on developing long-duration maintenance programmes and schedules. Chapter IV presents a selection of the most appropriate strategies including financial policy, time management, planning and work implementation, responsibilities and contracts, factors affecting traffic management including human factors. Chapter V provides an inventory of traffic management techniques under the prevailing circumstances of the work zone, with a distinction between long duration roadworks and short duration or mobile operations. Based on research and experience, it specifies efficient standard techniques ensuring acceptable levels of safety. The purpose of Chapter VI is to identify the general provisions for traffic control devices helping to ensure the safety and efficient movement of all traffic throughout the road transport system during work zone activities. A number of conclusions and recommendations are put forward in Chapter VII. Four Annexes provide technical information relating to traffic modelling in QUADRO 2 (U.K.), the traffic control plan in the U.S., road work information leaflets and commonly used traffic management techniques. As a whole, this report constitutes an up-to-date compendium of recent research and practical expertise on traffic operations and safety management at road work zones providing a basis for future national highway maintenance programmes and policies.

Subject classification: 10; 61; 73; 85

Fields: Economics and administration; equipment and maintenance methods; road safety devices; traffic control.

Keywords: Administration; construction site; cost benefit analysis; driver information; evaluation (assessment); financing; highway; maintenance; mathematical model; planning; safety; traffic control; traffic flow; traffic restraint.

ROAD TRANSPORT RESEARCH

traffic management and safety at highway work zones

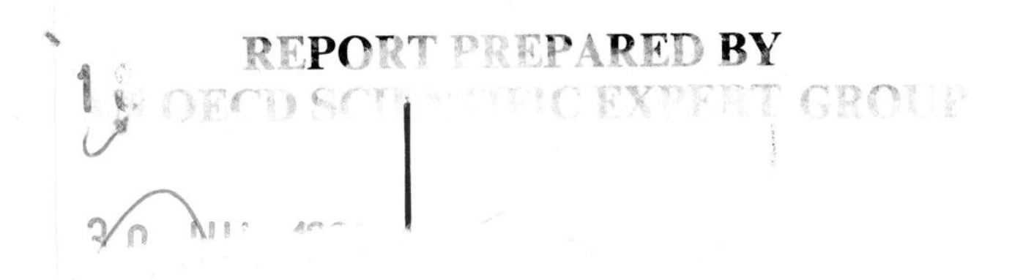

ORGANISATION FOR ECONOMIC CO-OPERATION AND DEVELOPMENT

Pursuant to article 1 of the Convention signed in Paris on 14th December 1960, and which came into force on 30th September 1961, the Organisation for Economic Co-operation and Development (OECD) shall promote policies designed:

- to achieve the highest sustainable economic growth and employment and a rising standard of living in Member countries, while maintaining financial stability, and thus to contribute to the development of the world economy;
- to contribute to sound economic expansion in Member as well as non-member countries in the process of economic development; and
- to contribute to the expansion of world trade on a multilateral, non-discriminatory basis in accordance with international obligations.

The original Member countries of the OECD are Austria, Belgium, Canada, Denmark, France, the Federal Republic of Germany, Greece, Iceland, Ireland, Italy, Luxembourg, the Netherlands, Norway, Portugal, Spain, Sweden, Switzerland, Turkey, the United Kingdom and the United States. The following countries became Members subsequently through accession at the dates indicated hereafter: Japan (28th April 1964), Finland (28th January 1969), Australia (7th June 1971) and New Zealand (29th May 1973).

The Socialist Federal Republic of Yugoslavia takes part in some of the work of the OECD (agreement of 28th October 1961).

Publié en français sous le titre :

GESTION DE LA CIRCULATION ET SÉCURITÉ ROUTIÈRE AU DROIT DES ZONES SOUS CHANTIER

EXECUTIVE SUMMARY

Road traffic continues to increase in most countries, frequently causing saturated or near-capacity operating conditions. The road networks suffering the most are often those whose infrastructure is becoming of age. This is particularly true for major motorways whose economic viability depends on the provision of adequate levels of service. Maintaining and repairing these roads and their equipment demands increasingly frequent and extensive roadworks.

In order to organise roadworks under conditions that are tolerable to users and economically acceptable, a major effort is required to find solutions appropriate to each situation: comprehensive schemes for work zones and temporary traffic operations, technological innovations, monitoring user behaviour and traffic, etc.

An exchange of relevant experiences and recent findings among Member countries provided a significant opportunity for comparing approaches and harmonising recommendations in such areas as:

- Accident statistics and measures to ensure safety of on-site workers and road users (number and type of accidents, risk factors and type of behaviour);

- Methods for traffic analysis and cost evaluation (traffic data bases, cost/benefit methods, simulations and modelling of work);

- Strategies and general organisation of traffic control schemes at highway work zones (preliminary studies and financial incentives, traffic forecasts and work schedules, project co-ordination, training and information);

- Traffic management techniques and standard procedures (lane closure and lane alteration, diversion, speed control, etc.);

- Use of and requirements for traffic control devices and safety equipment (signs and channelising devices, marking and lighting, safety barriers and crash cushions, etc.).

This overview of current practice and research covered functional and technical aspects as well as legal and economic. Such an analysis allowed the group to propose a comprehensive terminology of operations, to highlight some major developments and convergent trends and to pinpoint areas requiring research. The general report summarises these findings, frames recommendations for harmonising procedures and puts forward proposals, both in regard to control and safety measures and to evaluation and planning methods.

In most countries, traffic management has become a major element in planning and implementation of road works, demanding a high level of co-ordination, and involving many innovations in techniques and equipment. However, some gaps still remain in knowledge, particularly concerning traffic flow phenomena and drivers' behaviour, and there is still research needed towards improving the cost-effectiveness of safety and traffic control measures.

Nevertheless, it is now possible to reverse the general rule of previous decades, and state as a basic principle that "the work activities should adapt to traffic constraints". Technical choices for implementation of roadworks are becoming less dominant, and traffic management or drivers' service rise as leading priorities, especially on heavily trafficked major motorways. Their aim is not only to decrease users' inconvenience and costs, but also to increase users' awareness and measures' efficiency.

Detailed conclusions and recommendations presented in the report could be summarised in the following objectives:

- To study traffic and accidents in work zones, so as to develop priorities and to enhance strategies and traffic operation techniques. This involves developing data bases at more detailed or local level, improving the quality of both traffic management procedures and motorists' behaviour, comparing levels of risk, inconvenience and dissatisfaction.

- To assess and plan operations so as to optimise their costs and benefits; this can be accomplished by developing methods and models for traffic forecasts and indirect user costs, harmonizing basic cost values and costing criteria and selecting operation schemes for road works.

- To prepare actions and integrate traffic management from the design to the implementation stage of the work programme, in order to improve the level of service. This can be done by co-ordinating the choice of road work periods with other works, avoiding lane reductions or diversions and training workers.

- To inform drivers both before and during their trip through the work zone, so as to reduce unexpected incidents and inconvenience effects. This task requires improving traffic monitoring and incident detection, organising rapid rescue and protection, and techniques assessing warning and communication.

- To clarify and increase credibility of measures, so as to improve driver guidance and obedience. This can be obtained by ensuring the visibility and continuity of signs and channelisation, simplifying drivers' decisions and manoeuvres, eliminating unrealistic speed limits, and harmonizing measures through different networks.

- To promote new equipment and innovations, so as to suit better to the actual driver's behaviour and local conditions; increasing tests and experiments on breakability and safety, highlighting easiness of placing and removal of signing devices using complementary or redundant material for safety purposes.

All these research and development tasks need to be harmonized in the main OECD areas having a high proportion of international or inter-regional transit traffic (eg. Europe, North America, etc.), so that drivers can understand and obey the safety rules and messages and traffic control systems put along road works.

The development of economic evaluation techniques and traffic management schemes, calls for the adoption of an integrated approach, in which various interactions can be taken into account, and procedures be more acceptable to users.

TABLE OF CONTENTS

Page

Page

Chapter I

INTRODUCTION

I.1. CURRENT SITUATION

Road traffic continues to increase in most countries, frequently causing saturated or near-capacity operating conditions. The road networks suffering the most are often those whose infrastructure is becoming of age. This is particularly true for major motorways whose economic viability depends on the provision of adequate levels of service. Maintaining and repairing these roads and their equipment demands increasingly frequent and extensive roadworks. During such works, traffic flow and safety can be adversely affected by:

- -- Increased traffic congestion as a result of reduced route and/or network capacity, and this in spite of measures to compensate for capacity reductions such as work-free periods -- peak hours, weekends, holidays -- and appropriate traffic controls ;
- -- Increased dangers to drivers facing unfamiliar traffic and road situations as well as construction workers and equipment;
- -- Increased risk potential for workers, although relatively few accidents involving workers are severe.

There is a need to improve the overall management of roadworks in a way which is both, satisfactory to road users and economically acceptable. Large-scale operations have therefore been initiated in Member countries with new developments, regarding the overall design of work zones, techniques for temporary operation, technological innovations, monitoring of driver behaviour, traffic flow measurements, etc. Information on such developments, pilot projects and the experience acquired is invaluable and need to be exchanged between Member countries. A first OECD report was issued in 1973 (1), but it is recognised that further harmonization of proven practice would be beneficial to all parties concerned including those managing the road works, those overseeing traffic operations and, last but not least, the motorists.

In order to minimise inconvenience to road users and accident risk, traffic operations at work zones should employ the most suitable means aimed at resolving the potential conflicts between roadwork productivity and motorists' needs. The development and implementation of appropriate traffic operation measures cannot be separated from roadwork design and practice; a balance must be achieved between the following:

-- Traffic flow and road user inconvenience;

-- Safety of motorists and workers;

-- Efficient road work scheduling and economic traffic operation.

Temporary traffic control measures at and near the activity area may include -- depending on the traffic operation scheme chosen -- the following:

-- Speed limits, stopping of traffic or parking bans;

-- Reduction in the number or width of lanes;

-- Shuttle operation on one lane, controlled either by workers or by signs and signals;

-- Altered road layout by narrowing lanes or contra-flow operation;

-- Partial or total traffic detour to adjoining roads;

-- Construction of an additional, temporary lane(s) on the shoulder(s).

It should be mentioned that traffic diversion is not an ideal solution since alternative routes often have limited capacity, require longer journeys and do not offer the same level of safety. Shifting traffic to another carriageway or narrowing lanes, are costly to introduce, but are becoming of widespread acceptance because of the flow capacities which can be achieved.

The use of night-time works is increasing on urban highways, where traffic volumes are high throughout the day.

It will thus be seen that the choice of the traffic operation scheme at work zones, will be affected by the need to balance the three main factors present -- works, road and traffic -- and should be based on an assessment of overall generalised costs including both the direct costs of works and indirect costs related to user inconvenience. The economic evaluation of measures and their effects on traffic and safety, provides a yardstick with which different solutions can be compared and schedules fixed.

The implementation of the operational scheme chosen involves temporary traffic guidance devices and signs, as well as safety equipment and driver information means, whose general purpose is:

-- To assist in understanding roadway direction and avoid driver hesitation;

-- To remind drivers of the regulations in force, speed limits and channelisation of lanes;

-- To promote safety and segregation at points of conflict;

-- To inform users of foreseeable traffic disruptions and alternative routes.

Particular attention has been paid to temporary traffic control devices. This is now the subject of regulations based on a few fundamental principles:

-- Suitability to the situation and the type of works;

-- Consistency with permanent traffic signs and other information systems;

-- Adaptation to changing situations, including the return to normal conditions;

-- Avoiding information overloading by concentrating signs at the same location; legibility of signs under all weather and time conditions.

A wide range of temporary traffic control equipment is available. Apart from the introduction of specifications to ensure quality and reliability, studies are currently underway to harmonize equipment and introduce new or improved designs (improvements in visibility, ease of placing and removal, attenuating potential damage to vehicles, cost reductions, etc.):

-- Temporary road signs, variable message signs, work zone signals;

-- Road marking materials and their removal;

-- Rigid or flexible traffic guidance devices (cones, stakes, marker posts);

-- Traffic barriers to separate work space from travel area; they may be stationary or moveable and made of concrete or plastic material;

-- Work site clothing.

The application of these devices and their continuous monitoring, particularly in the case of major roadworks, requires enhanced traffic surveillance using detectors, video cameras, etc., as well as the planning of rapid means of intervention.

Finally, the particular hazards associated with roadworks make it necessary that the workers be well-trained, and motorists' awareness of the special driving conditions be systematically enhanced.

I.2. SCOPE AND OBJECTIVES OF THE STUDY

Because of the increasing national and international dimension of the issues involved, there is a need to update present knowledge and experience in the field, with particular reference to:

-- Regulatory aspects and job management;

-- Accident occurrence and safety improvements;

-- Effective and innovative traffic control techniques and equipment;

-- Economic analysis and long-term implications of strategies designed to meet the increasing needs for maintenance and repair of road systems.

Because approaches to safety and traffic control at work zones differ between Member countries, an exchange of experience is essential. As stated in the OECD Terms of Reference, the aim of this study is to examine and compare current practices, and to determine their implications for safety, their economic impacts and their effects on traffic flow.

This study covers all interurban road networks, particularly major roads and motorways, where traffic volumes are high and the problems most severe. Included in this analysis are urban expressways, but the urban street network is excluded.

Different types of roadworks are examined, from mobile and short duration to long duration roadworks. Short-duration roadworks are generally defined as lasting less than one-day shifts; it is, however, widely agreed that, should there be a risk to prolong them into night, they should either be shut down or treated as fixed works.

The broad tasks of this study were:

-- A review of traffic control measures used on divided highways, (motorways, expressways), or individual highways with two-way traffic. Impacts of these methods on traffic flow, and technical or procedural innovations introduced by private contractors or road authorities, will be reviewed, including:

  . Operating procedures, regulations and technical guidelines;

  . Equipment and accessories used for temporary signing, traffic guidance and the protection of workers;

  . User information (type of information, data collection and dissemination).

-- A review of safety measures (which are closely linked to the above):

  . Survey of traffic accident data regarding work zones;

  . Analysis of accident factors involved in regard to both, workers and drivers;

  . Inventory of measures taken to improve safety.

-- A review of costs and economic impacts of traffic and safety measures, as well as work zone arrangements and maintenance procedures:

  . Collecting available data;

  . Optimising selection of traffic control techniques;

  . Overall long-term strategies for the planning of roadworks.

I.3. STRUCTURE OF THE REPORT

The Working Group, who consisted of scientific experts from Member countries, began by assembling the experience and knowledge of each country in the form of national submissions. From this basis it was possible to examine and discuss the topics addressed in this report. It should be noted that the terminology used has been chosen from a glossary of work zone terms (2).

On the basis of the assessment of the major issues and basic accident and traffic flow data, it was possible to identify the main problems from the viewpoints of safety, traffic control and economic impacts.

Chapter II discusses road safety problems with reference to both overall risks and more specific risks relating to a particular operating mode or type of behaviour. The studies referred to pay particular attention to major roadworks on motorways.

Chapter III reviews traffic and cost-evaluation data bases and methods, including methodologies for traffic volume analysis, cost/benefit assessment or modelling for work zone planning.

Chapter IV outlines the principal components of strategies, including: preliminary studies and contractual clauses, financial incentives, co-ordination of schedules and locations, choice of operating schemes, worker training and driver information. (The way these strategies are implemented depends on the operating technique selected and equipment used.)

Chapter V examines traffic operation techniques with due regard to conditions of application -- reducing speed, narrowing of lanes -- and different procedures such as shifting traffic to a different carriageway, contra-flow, shuttle operation or diversion.

Chapter VI presents traffic and safety equipment with conditions for its use and requirements such as visibility and ease of placing, lowering potential of vehicle damage in the event of a collision, etc.

Chapter VII contains the conclusions and recommendations of this report, major developments, research needs and harmonization requirements, as they have been identified through the joint comparative assessment of experience.

REFERENCES

1. OECD. ROAD RESEARCH. Traffic operation at sites of temporary obstruction. OECD. Paris, 1973.

2. LEWIS, RM. Work zone traffic control concepts and terminology. 68th Annual Meeting of the Transportation Research Board. Transportation Research Board. Washington, DC, 1989.

Chapter II

SAFETY ISSUES

II.1. GENERAL

The assessment and interpretation of traffic accident data concerning roadworks remain one of the major difficulties when attempting to determine the scale of the safety problem. Differences in criteria and analysis techniques mean that it is difficult to compare the results from different countries in a meaningful way.

From some of the national reports it is noticeable that although there are many general comments about safety at work zones there are relatively few detailed accident analyses. Where accidents occur the police are only called to record accidents involving fatalities, injuries or extensive damage. As a result, the majority of accidents involving only minor damage are not included in statistical road safety analyses and the number of accidents occurring at highway work zones tends to be underestimated.

II.2. ACCIDENT SURVEYS

Most Member countries do not possess precise and specific records from which reliable conclusions on accidents at work zones can be drawn. It is still possible, however, to observe some general trends on the basis of studies of typical examples of work zones (mobile, short duration, long duration, etc.) where accident analyses have been carried out.

For example, the United Kingdom has undertaken specific surveys on several 2x3-lane motorway sites undergoing major works involving shifting traffic to the opposing carriageway and contra-flow operation. According to this study (1):

-- The rate of personal injury accidents (per million vehicle.km) is about 1.5 higher over the entire length of a work zone (i.e. 6 km before, the section with two-way traffic and 6 km after) than the rate noted on the same road section under normal conditions.

-- This rate is not uniform along the whole length of the work zone and depends on the length and geometry of crossover and contra-flow sections with two-way traffic. Despite the increased accident rate due to the presence of roadworks on motorways, the risk is still appreciably less than that encountered elsewhere on the non-motorway network; for example, the motorway work rate is lower than the no-work rate on major urban roads, and rural roads. This factor should be taken into account when alternative routing is considered.

Comparable results have been obtained in an investigation of 8 000 accidents occurring on a total of 226 motorway work zones in Germany (9). The results are presented in Table II.1. The operating system 4+0 lanes (i.e. one carriageway under construction; four lanes on the other carriageway with the following operating system: two lanes in one direction and two lanes in the other direction), is the most dangerous. This study has also provided detailed information on accident rates for the four areas of a work zone, as defined in Figure IV.2.

Table II.1.

ACCIDENT RATE FACTOR* AS A FUNCTION OF THE MOST COMMON TRAFFIC OPERATING SYSTEMS

Traffic operating system **	Accident rate factor			
	Serious personal injury	Slight personal injury	Severe property damage	Total damage
2 + 2	0.7	1.4	1.7	1.5
3 + 1	0.8	1.2	1.7	1.5
4 + 0	1.1	1.9	2.2	2.0

* $\text{Accident rate factor} = \frac{\text{accident rate for work zones}}{\text{accident rate for free motorway section}}$

** 2 + 2 = 2 lanes per carriageway
3 + 1 = 3 lanes on 1 carriageway of which 1 is contra-flow; 1 lane on the other carriageway.
4 + 0 = All lanes on the same carriageway: 2 in one direction and 2 in the other.

In a more recent investigation in Germany covering multiple accidents on the German motorway network for the years 1980-1985, it was found that work zones have generally a higher accident risk with predominant types of accidents. 6.4 per cent of all accidents on German motorways, 11.6 per cent of multiple vehicle accidents (i.e. involving at least 8 persons within a distance of 200 m) and 24 per cent of all chain collisions (i.e. happening within a distance of 4 000 m and within a period of 90 mn.) occur at work zones. It should however be noted that over the period of the investigation these types of accidents have been decreasing (10).

The rate of damage-only accidents is probably double or treble the one on the same road section with unimpeded traffic. The majority of accidents are rear-end collisions. These may make up 40 to 50 per cent of all accidents (2). Another type of accident which rarely features in most national statistics is collisions with the work zone traffic guidance system. As a rule this type of accident produces little damage or personal injury (3). Broken down or damaged vehicles in a work zone often give rise to secondary collisions.

Finally, the results of a Swedish survey are noteworthy, showing that nearly 75 per cent of road workers are afraid to work on work zones located on motorways (11).

II.3. EFFECT OF SPEED

The following trends are apparent:

-- Excessive speeds and reduced headways between vehicles increase accident rates at work zones as well as accidents in which road workers are involved. Speed limits should be clearly indicated at the roadside and introduced progressively upstream of the work zone, so that traffic continues to flow freely and vehicles remain evenly spaced;

-- Entrances and exits for work vehicles should be carefully designed to be as safe as possible, for the safety of both personnel and vehicles. To ensure this it is important to provide a well-marked deceleration lane at the work zone entrance and an acceleration lane for rejoining the traffic stream at the exit, as this manoeuvre can also be a major cause of accidents;

-- In several countries buffer zones, crash cushions or barriers are placed at the beginning of the activity area. Their aim is to protect working personnel by ensuring that vehicles do not enter this area (4, 5);

Further comments on the effects of speed in work zones are to be found in Chapter V.

II.4. WORK ZONE CHARACTERISTICS AND GENERAL DRIVING CONDITIONS

II.4.1. Traffic engineering

The work zone should be noticeable from a long distance so that the road user can react suitably, and gradually reduce his speed, if needed.

For this to occur, various points should be thoroughly examined:

-- The position (alignment and profile) and length of the work zone;

-- The location of the work zone; the number of lanes and their widths in the work zone (reduction in the number of lanes, geometry of crossover section, etc.);

-- When using a crossover section:

.The length and design of the crossover zone;
.The length of the contra-flow section;
.The quality of signing and road marking;

-- The duration of roadworks also affects the number and rate of accidents. However, it should be noted that short duration roadworks -- lasting less than one day and which are often poorly signed -- have high accident potential.

II.4.2. General driving conditions

Traffic safety at work zones also depends on various factors such as: meteorological conditions (rain, fog, ice, snow, etc.); volume of traffic and temporal distribution of flows (peak periods, weekend traffic, public holidays, tourism):

-- On Fridays, Saturdays, Sundays or on public holidays (6) accident rates at work zones could be double, or even treble, what they are on normal days of the week;

-- The accident rate could be double during the evening rush hours. During the morning peak period, the rate only increases slightly;

-- At night, in the early hours of the morning, the accident rate is considerably higher than the daily mean and in the period immediately before midnight;

-- Accident rates for mobile and short-duration roadworks are well above the average, especially at daily peak periods.

II.4.3. Night driving

Site illumination and good visibility of signs and vehicle movements are of fundamental importance to safety at work zones. However, studies of this subject have not established satisfactorily the link between road lighting, site illumination and traffic safety.

The basic principle involved is that perception of the work zone from a distance and user guidance through the work zone, should be as good at night as during the day (4). Generally, there is no specific requirement for road lighting for work zones outside built-up areas, except for sites with a particularly high accident risk.

In all cases work zone traffic signs should be illuminated, or at least retroreflective. The technical features of lighting systems are discussed in greater detail in Chapter VI.

II.5. POTENTIAL SAFETY IMPROVEMENTS

It has been established that the presence of work zones increase the accident risk to the public. The above discussion shows that experience gained provides a few indications as to how the number and duration of roadworks could be reduced, and with this the number of road accidents related to road construction and maintenance.

II.5.1. Traffic engineering

Accidents on contra-flow and especially on crossover sections are particularly serious. It is therefore necessary to physically separate opposing traffic flows using raised devices (high density of cones or marker posts, barriers, etc.).

Multiple collisions occur at the end of queues, the lengths of which are varying. It is therefore advisable to indicate the position of the end of a queue by means of a mobile warning device such as, for example, the remote-controlled "MOWESI" system (see Chapter VI) or other suitable signs which would warn users sufficiently early to enable them to alter their behaviour, if necessary.

Where the cross section is reduced, broken down or damaged vehicles must be removed from traffic lanes as quickly as possible. For this purpose it is advisable to provide for special spaces to contain these vehicles before the arrival of the emergency removal service. Traffic monitoring at work zones is essential in this situation.

To reduce congestion on major roads, works should be kept to a minimum or avoided altogether in daily or seasonal peak periods.

Some countries have laid down guidelines banning road works on major roads in peak periods if the carriageway could be reduced to less than four lanes (2, 4).

Warning signs should be basically pictograms so as to be understood by all road users, including foreign drivers.

It is important that the work zone signing should be checked and maintained with particular care. Good results have been obtained by using a video camera mounted on a vehicle travelling at the advised speed for the work zone to record a driver's eye view of the layout and to draw attention to those sections which may need adjustment.

II.5.2. Reduction of users' speed

Speed limits at work zones are frequently ignored. Additional measures should therefore be considered to oblige drivers to slow down. The police use of radar to prevent offences and the narrowing of lanes or construction of obstacles can be mentioned as examples. There are however some reservations about these latter methods from the point of view of effectiveness and ease of implementation. Another possibility is to install variable message signs (VMS) to remind drivers of the speed limit, or better still to display their actual speed (7), though these devices may loose their effectiveness with time.

II.5.3. Work zone set up and job management

It should be remembered that a preliminary study should cover the entire work zone, concentrating mainly on the traffic data from which the number of lanes which should remain open to traffic is determined (4).

Where there is a likelihood of congestion, it is preferable to reduce lane widths rather than their number, so as to retain the highest possible traffic flow capacity. The existing emergency stopping lanes may be used for traffic or new provisional road systems created (4, 6).

When a work zone is on an upgrade, particular attention should be paid to reductions in cross section where there is a high percentage of heavy vehicles, as the risk of congestion is increased.

II.6. CONCLUSIONS

II.6.1. Principles

The safety philosophy at work zones could be summed up by the maxim "It is the worksite which should adapt, if possible, to traffic conditions, and not the traffic which should adapt to the worksite!" (4).

This implies that:

-- Roadworks should be carefully planned and carried out at times when traffic volumes are lower. Roadworks should, where possible, be banned during the high holiday season, at weekends and at rush hours;

-- The duration of roadworks should be as limited as possible;

-- Poor traffic devices are often a contributory factor to accidents at work zones. Safety performance can be enhanced by paying attention not only to the conspicuity and location of these devices, but also to their design and material to reduce the risk of serious damage in a collision (see Chapter VI).

-- For night-time works, the period prior to midnight should be preferred to that after midnight, because of increased accident rates;

-- Short duration roadworks require special attention. Their signing should be particularly careful as local road users may be surprised by roadworks of this type and respond abruptly or in an unexpected manner;

-- For each work zone a well-qualified person must be put in charge of safety aspects concerning road construction and maintenance and the monitoring and directing of the traffic passing the work zone (4, 5).

II.6.2. Research requirements

-- The analysis of a broad range of experience has produced a considerable number of remarks and items of information on improving traffic safety at work zones. However, details about accidents in these zones are very limited. Therefore, specific, regular studies of these accidents should be undertaken which make distinctions between the following:

. Advance warning and transition areas (with space for deceleration, with or without reduction in the number of lanes, zones of congestion);

. Crossover sections where lanes are moved or shifted onto the opposite carriageway, or back to their normal path;

. Zones of channelised traffic, especially with contraflows;

. Zones which are illuminated to improve safety;

. Mobile, short duration and night-time roadworks (for example lasting from half to one day).

-- The resulting improved understanding of causes and hazards would enable appropriate solutions to be found. However, it is already possible to identify certain situations where particular care is essential, especially on major roads:

. Zones where lane channelisation begins and carriageway switching takes place (guidance and physical separation of lanes);

. Channelised and contra-flow road sections (traffic guidance system, barriers, vehicle refuges, monitoring and rapid intervention in the event of an incident);

. Risk of rear-end collisions, where there is congestion (traffic surveillance, detection and information, end of queue warning, additional traffic control or diversion measures).

-- As speed modification measures are not always very effective, it would be helpful to increase the exchange of experiences in order to establish the effects of:

- Physical alteration of lanes (obstacles, reduced width, marginal friction caused by traffic guidance systems, etc.);
- Operations to increase driver awareness and knowledge (risks taken, good practices, possible penalties, site monitoring, warning of inconvenience, etc.).

-- On more minor roads the emphasis should mainly be placed on checking and improving measures to ensure that they remain effective and in tune with changes in work zones and traffic.

REFERENCES

1. SUMMERSGILL, I. Safety performance of traffic management at major road-works on motorways in 1982. Report RR 42. Transport and Road Research Laboratory. Crowthorne, 1985.

2. WEBER. German National Report. Bundesministerium für Verkehr. Bonn, 1987.

3. FHWA. United States National Report. Chapter 10 -- Construction and Maintenance Zones. Federal Highway Administration. Washington, DC, December 1982.

4. BASEL, AG and NEUCHATEL, AJS. Massnahmen zur Aufrechterhaltung des Verkehrs im Bereich von Bauarbeiten an Autobahnen und Strassen. Report VSS No. 09187. Zürich, April 1987.

5. US DEPARTMENT OF TRANSPORTATION. Design and operation of work zone traffic control. Participant notebook. US Department of Transportation. Washington, DC.

6. HOOGVORST, A. Dutch National Report. Rijkswaterstaat. The Hague, 1987.

7. CAUBET, C and GRANDJEAN, M. French National Report. Paris, 1987.

8. McGUINNESS, P. Traffic control at roadworks. Dublin, September 1984.

9. EMDE, W, and HAMESTER, H. Unfallgeschehen an Autobahnbaustellen. Informationen Verkehrsplanung und Strassenwesen. Hochschule der Bundeswehr München. Heft 14. Münich, 1983.

10. ERNST, G, BRÜHNING, E and HEUSER, W.
Massen-und Serienunfälle auf BAB - Ergebnisse für die Jahre 1980-1985.
Strassenverkehrstechnick. Heft 1/1989.
Bad Godesberg, Jan.-Feb., 1989.

11. SWEDISH FOUNDATION FOR OCCUPATIONAL HEALTH AND SAFETY FOR STATE EMPLOYEES (Statshälsan). Health hazards among road workers in Sweden. Borlänge, 1986.

Chapter III

TRAFFIC ANALYSIS AND COST EVALUATION

III.1. INTRODUCTION

Knowledge of road traffic characteristics is becoming an increasingly important need for all countries, not only to ensure the safe operation of their road networks and to plan for appropriate investment in improvements, but also to assist with the scheduling and design of work zones.

When determining the form and timing of such projects, full account must be taken of their effects on the safety of road users and of the need to minimise the possible disruption of traffic.

The aim of traffic management at major road works is to obtain a balance between providing adequate space for the contractor to carry out the work safely, economically and speedily, while also allowing traffic to flow safely and without undue delay.

In order to achieve these aims, reference is made to traffic flow records in the area at an early stage in the planning of the works. Traffic count data are often available from national sources, since many countries have a system of permanent automatic counter sites on their primary network, collecting continuous flow information. However, the form and coverage of these counts vary from country to country.

III.2. ROAD DATABASES

In addition to these basic flow records, many countries are currently developing road databases as part of their overall plan for monitoring maintenance and management of their road systems (21). At present, the data content varies between countries, though the common core (including the network description) generally consists of information on traffic volumes, traffic accidents, road condition survey results and road bridge characteristics.

In the United Kingdom, for example, much data relating to road characteristics and the state of roads are stored in a variety of forms by both County Councils and the Department of Transport. In order to make more efficient use of existing data and to obtain maximum value from the limited funds and resources available, the Department of Transport is developing, for the primary road network of motorways and other trunk roads, a Network

Information System (NIS) (1). It will consist of two main categories: operational -- traffic and accident data -- and inventory -- "as-built" records of new roads and major maintenance works, geometry of road layout, road lighting, etc.

Several County Councils are also developing similar information systems for their own local roads and there is close collaboration between these authorities and the Department of Transport to ensure that, wherever possible, the different systems will be able to communicate with each other.

In France, a decision was taken in 1975 to establish a road database for the entire national road system (28 000 km), whose coverage was completed by 1987. The comprehensive catalogue of information includes; details on road geometry, general characteristics, traffic, accidents, construction and maintenance works, and pavement condition.

A similar system was initiated in Sweden in 1974 and now covers approximately 100 000 km of roads. Details recorded include road geometry and pavement, condition survey results, bridge information, traffic and accident data (2).

Traffic and safety data are also held in the Highway Pavement Monitoring System (HPMS) used in the United States. The information is used for the general scheduling of road projects and the determination of long-term requirements for maintenance and investment on State and Federal highways.

A centralised database has recently been established in the Netherlands, detailing information on pavement materials and age, surface state and traffic. A few local road databases relating to some provinces and major towns have also been developed.

In Belgium, preliminary work has commenced to determine the objectives and content of a road database.

The Spanish road information system is based on two types of data store: a database containing information relating to the physical characteristics of different routes and sections of the network; and videotapes illustrating the state and characteristics of the road and its environment.

Since 1984, in Germany, geometric data from the federal trunk roads has been logged using specialised vehicles, but generally the data banks are regionally located.

Similarly, the Australian system set up by the National Association of Australian State Road Authorities (NAASRA) is not a single national entity, stored at a central point, but a series of co-ordinated data banks of individual road authorities.

When fully developed, these databases will offer detailed sources of static and dynamic link information to which engineers can refer at the planning stage of their maintenance programme.

III.3. GENERAL APPLICATION OF TRAFFIC DATA

In many cases, as part of the preparatory works prior to the start of the maintenance programme, national and regional data are supplemented by local counts taken on the links where the work activities are scheduled, and also on the surrounding network which may be affected.

Additional monitoring of flows at major junctions in the vicinity of the proposed works, may also need to be considered. Some count estimates may be required for the local network during weekend and holiday periods, or on other occasions when the normal flow pattern is disrupted (sporting events, exhibitions, etc.).

These flow records (local and national) provide a source for details of traffic distributions over a range of time periods -- a day, week, month or year -- and, where appropriate, can provide estimates for local traffic growth rates to predict traffic demand which will relate to works programmed in the immediate future.

The flow information should be classified by vehicle type, with particular reference to heavy freight vehicles, to assist with decisions regarding the allocation of lane widths through the works, the need for the introduction of traffic segregation, and the possible use of diversions (see also Chapter V for further considerations when planning maintenance work).

Experience in the United Kingdom has shown that 24-hour count information is more appropriate to works planning than the alternative 16-hour count which is limited to the peak and daytime off-peak periods. Whilst it is necessary to know the flows during the peak periods to assess whether the proposed road-work layout can cope with the demand, an appreciation of the traffic levels during low-flow periods at night is also needed, in order to efficiently schedule changeovers between phases of major traffic management systems with the minimum of traffic disruption.

Comparisons of demand flows during the works period with the capacity of the proposed system will give an indication whether delays can be expected, and their possible magnitude. If periods of queueing are likely to arise, then the works method may have to be reviewed, adjusting the traffic management system, and/or the scheduling of the maintenance programme.

Measurements of the average hourly vehicular throughput at work zones in Germany (3), the United Kingdom (4), and the United States (5), are given in Table III.1, together with the operational design capacities employed at Swiss and French work zones.

However, whilst some guidance on scheduling and layout may be obtained by these comparisons of traffic demand and operational capacity, and there may be occasions when specific reasons dictate the selection of a particular site layout, it is more efficient to base the choice on overall cost considerations, i.e. the cost of both providing and operating the system.

Table III.1

MAXIMUM THROUGHPUTS (in veh/h) OBSERVED FOR DIFFERENT CARRIAGEWAY ARRANGEMENTS*

Type of layout	Maximum throughput veh/h	veh/h/lane
United Kingdom		
Observations at motorway work sites (1)		
Lane closure -- 1 lane open	1 650	1 650
-- 2 lanes open	3 280	1 640
2-way traffic (one lane each way)	1 540	1 540
Segregated contra-flow (primary) (2)	2 980	1 490
Full contra-flow (primary)	3 040	1 520
Contra-flow (secondary)	3 080	1 540
United States		
3 lane to 1 lane reduction	1 170	1 170
2 lane to 1 lane reduction	1 340	1 340
5 lane to 2 lane reduction	2 740	1 370
4 lane to 2 lane reduction	2 960	1 480
3 lane to 2 lane reduction	2 980	1 490
4 lane to 3 lane reduction	4 560	1 520
Switzerland and Germany (3)		
With works (operational design capacities):		
2 lane to 1 lane reduction	1 100	1 100
3 lane to 2 lane reduction	2 400	1 200
Without works:		
Single lane capacity	1 300	1 300
2 lane capacity	2 700	1 350
3 lane capacity	4 200	1 400
France		
Maximum throughput, with works in progress: 1 500 to 1 600 veh/h/lane		
Works traffic management systems arranged such that lanes do not exceed an operational limit of 1 200 veh/h/lane		

* This table illustrates a typical range of national traffic counts at work zones according to specific lane arrangements.

1. Observed flows have 15 per cent heavy freight vehicles.
2. The "primary" direction is the direction of the carriageway on which the work is to be done.
3. Applies to lanes < 3.5 m wide; the maximum traffic volumes with wider lanes can be up to 14 per cent higher.

III.4. COST EVALUATION CONSIDERATIONS

The total cost of major road maintenance comprises two principal elements:

.. The capital cost of undertaking the work (direct cost); this will include, for example, the cost of materials, plant, labour, traffic management layout and signing, etc., and is usually met by central or local government.

.. The second element, which can be just as important, is the cost imposed on the road users while the road works are being carried out. This user cost is associated with delays, changes in vehicle operating costs and accidents.

Thus when assessing maintenance costs, the cost of the works and its related road user costs should be taken into account.

In many countries, whilst expenditure on new road building has declined over the past few years, expenditure on road maintenance is increasing. This is due to an increase in heavy freight vehicle traffic, the ageing of the primary network, and the increase in the size of the network as schemes are completed.

At the same time it is evident that a major cost of maintenance is borne by road users, in terms of traffic delays. It is very important that with limited public sector resources, the aim should be to achieve maximum value for money from this expenditure on major trunk road maintenance, in both works and user cost terms.

Equally, future maintenance requirements can have significant implications for current road building programmes and these should be taken into account. An efficient roads programme should avoid the needs for major reconstruction, where possible, by planning earlier minor repairs and resurfacing. There is also the need to look at costs of new roads over their whole life, as distinct from just their initial construction costs, by taking into account maintenance aspects.

The prime consideration in these evaluations is the increase in travel time, as a result of slower running through the works section, and the additional time associated with an alternative route, should diversion of traffic occur. The lower journey speeds, in turn, also give rise to changes in vehicle operating costs. In addition, the number of accidents may also alter as a result of the works and the extra travel on the diversion route, which may already have a higher accident rate than the main route. These three basic cost elements (time lost, vehicle operating costs, and accidents) form the foundation of the cost evaluations. The following sections deal with each of these items, and comment on their derivation and application.

III.5. COST EVALUATION ELEMENTS

III.5.1. The value of time

The time spent in travelling has a value to the occupants of all vehicles on the network. The value of time plays an important role when evaluating the total costs for the community.

A number of approaches and theories exist on parameters and criteria used in the development of concepts of value of time for various socio-economic classes of individuals. It should be noted that the value of time can vary from one country to another depending upon the national context.

For example, in the United Kingdom, the criterion is "willingness to pay". This value, however, will depend on the purpose of the journey; two distinct travel purposes are used in cost calculations:

-- Travel in the course of work (known as working time); and

-- Travel for all other purposes, including commuting to and from work (non-working time).

Working time is valued at the cost to an employer of a travelling employee. It has a value equal to a national average gross wage rate (before tax deductions), weighted by the amount of travel of road users in different income groups, plus an allowance for employers' overheads.

The value of non-working time is derived from studies of people's behaviour (6, 7) when they are faced with a trade-off between time and cost of travel; for example, the choice between a slow, but cheap, mode of travel and a faster but more expensive one.

Studies conducted in the United Kingdom suggest that, on average, people value savings of in-vehicle non-working time at approximately one quarter of their gross hourly wage rates (excluding employers' overheads). The value used is therefore 25 per cent of the average travel weighted income of travellers.

When attributing a value to the travel time of vehicles, some account must be taken of the fact that different classes of vehicles are likely to contain a varying number of occupants, and travel on different purposes. For example, a light freight vehicle normally travels in the course of work and is likely to contain only the driver, whilst a car may have several occupants when on a leisure trip, or, most probably, only the driver when commuting to work. These variations in vehicle occupancy are overcome by dividing the traffic flow into vehicle types, each carrying an average number of occupants appropriate to that class.

Occupants of all light and other freight vehicles are considered to be travelling in working time. In the case of cars, national travel studies, in Sweden and the United Kingdom, have shown that about 15 per cent are travelling in the course of work, thus valuing the occupants' time as working, and approximately 85 per cent are travelling on other purposes, when the occupants' time is considered as non-working.

Several countries have determined values of time per vehicle. Examples of the rates used in France (8), Germany (9), Sweden and the United Kingdom (10), are given in Table III.2, together with the underlying assumptions about occupancy and the allocation of working/non-working time.

III.5.2. The valuation of vehicle operating costs

The change in total vehicle operating costs over the network depends on changes in distance travelled, and on variations in the average vehicle speed. Thus, for example, vehicle operating costs will tend to increase during maintenance works if speeds through the maintained section of road are very low or if the diversion route is lengthy.

Vehicle operating costs generally take account of six items: fuel, oil, tyres, maintenance, vehicle capital costs, and depreciation. All costs are in resource terms: that is, taxes, such as fuel duty and VAT, are excluded. Items which do not vary with the use of the vehicle are also omitted, e.g. vehicle excise duty, insurance, etc.

Operating costs in cost unit/km consist of:

-- Fixed items, such as oil, fuel, tyres, maintenance, and depreciation; and

-- Speed-related items, such as maintenance, fuel, and vehicle capital.

These elements can be classified into fuel and non-fuel items and the cost per vehicle-kilometre for each item estimated for individual vehicle classes.

Vehicle operating cost relationships of varying complexity have been derived in several countries, including Germany (9), the United Kingdom (10) and the United States (11). These functions give higher costs at low speeds, reflecting the effects of "stop-start" motoring in congested conditions. Adjustments are also made to the fuel element of operating costs for gradients and, in the case of light freight vehicles and cars, for constant running speeds on motorways (where fuel consumption is less, compared with the same speed on all-purpose roads).

III.5.3. The valuation of accident costs

Accidents, as well as causing traffic delays, have their own "direct" costs, reflecting the loss of output due to death or injury, costs incurred by the emergency services and by police and insurance administration, cost of damage to property, and a notional cost to represent the associated pain, grief and suffering.

Table III.2 (a)

VALUES OF TIME PER PERSON AND PER VEHICLE IN THE UNITED KINGDOM (PENCE/HOUR, AVERAGE 1986 LEVELS)

Type of vehicle	Occupancy	Type and value of time per occupant		Value of time per vehicle
Working car	1.00 driver	working	757.6	884.8
	0.21 passengers	working	605.8	
Non-working car	1.00 driver	non-working	161.2	301.4
	0.87 passengers	non-working	161.2	
Average car	1.00 driver	16.7 % working		398.8
	0.76 passengers	83.3 % non-working		
Light freight vehicle	1.00 driver	working	476.1	618.9
	0.30 passengers	working	476.1	
Other freight vehicle	1.00 driver	working	552.8	663.3
	0.20 passengers	working	552.8	
Public service vehicles	1.00 driver	working	510.0	2 994.3
	0.25 conductors	working	498.6	
	14.17 passengers	non-working	161.2	
	0.15 passengers	working	502.8	

Table III.2 (b)

VALUES OF TIME PER VEHICLE IN GERMANY (DM/HOUR)

Type of vehicle	Value of time per vehicle	
	Weekdays	Sundays
Average car (weighted value of working and non-working)	7.00	3.50
Light freight vehicle	30.00	-
Other freight vehicle	42.00	-
Public service vehicles	90.00	90.00

Table III.2 (c)

VALUES OF TIME PER PERSON AND PER VEHICLE IN SWEDEN
(SEK/HOUR, AVERAGE 1986 LEVELS)

Type of vehicle	Occupancy	Type and value of time per occupant		Value of time per vehicle
Urban Areas:				
Working car	1.00 driver	working	100	120
	0.20 passengers	working	100	
Non-working car	1.00 driver	non-working	12	21
	0.70 passengers	non-working	12	
Average car	1.00 driver	15 % working		36
	0.60 passengers	85 % non-working		
Light freight and other freight vehicles				102
Public service vehicle costs are calculated for each case, assuming a passenger (working/non-working) time value of 16.50				
Rural Areas:				
Working car	1.00 driver	working	100	140
	0.40 passengers	working	100	
Non-working car	1.00 driver	non-working	11	25
	1.20 passengers	non-working	11	
Average car	1.00 driver	15 % working		42
	1.10 passengers	85 % non-working		
Light freight and other freight vehicles				102
Public service vehicle information is not available				

Table III.2 (d)

VALUES OF TIME PER VEHICLE IN FRANCE (FF/HOUR)

Type of vehicle	Value of time per vehicle
Light freight vehicle -- perceived	50.00
-- resource	76.00
Heavy freight and public service vehicles	132.00

These costs arise in two ways:

.. Firstly, there may be an additional accident risk to the main traffic route associated with the work zone.

.. Secondly, traffic which diverts from the main route may well travel on roads of a lower standard and subject to a higher accident rate. This, coupled with the likelihood of the diversion route being longer than the main route, also points towards an increase in accidents as a result of the works.

Studies have shown that it is sensible to split the site-related accidents into two components (12):

.. The first corresponds to accidents along the work zone itself, reflecting the change in geometric standards of the carriageway. The number of accidents is dependent on the flow, the work length, and the accident rate -- expressed in Personal Injury Accident (PIA) per million vehicle-kilometres ("site-length" rate).

.. The second component is made up largely of accidents in the approaches and at the start of the work zone. These are independent of the work zone length and are calculated using the flow through the work zone and a rate expressed in PIA per million vehicles, which is a measure of the extra accidents associated with the presence of the site ("site-presence" rate).

The "normal" number of accidents on these sections is still calculated using the works-free rate, as shown in Figure III.1.

The cost of an accident varies with its severity in terms of both the number of vehicles and people involved, and the severity of the injuries sustained (9, 10, 11). Table III.3 shows the average casualty costs in Germany, Sweden, the United Kingdom and the United States.

Other items, which may be considered in an evaluation exercise, but which are more difficult to quantify, are the environmental impacts of the works on their surroundings -- for example, noise, air pollution, and, in urban situations, the effect on business.

It is only by taking into account more fully these factors, particularly time lost, vehicle operating costs and accidents, that a more representative works' costs estimate can be established and the full effect on users of the maintenance task quantified.

III.6. COST EVALUATION MODELS

To meet these objectives, methods of economic appraisal have been developed in a few countries, notably Germany, the United Kingdom and the United States.

The main economic appraisal procedures widely used in the United Kingdom are embodied in two Department of Transport computer programs, COBA9 (COst Benefit Analysis) (10) and QUADRO2 (QUeues And Delays at ROadworks) (13):

.. The former program is concerned with identification, evaluation and comparison of costs and benefits of new road schemes over a given period.

.. The second program, QUADRO2 provides a method of economic assessment of road maintenance. The program is compatible with COBA9 in that it uses the same economic and traffic parameters, so that in addition to assessing the full cost of different types and timing of works, it may also be applied to new road schemes, where the interest is in evaluating future maintenance implications of proposals for road widening or new road construction.

An outline of the main features of the QUADRO2 program is given in Annex A. The program models a simple network consisting of a main route, containing the work zone, and a representative diversion route around the works. The program is run with and without the works present, and evaluations are made for the differences in time and vehicle operating costs incurred by all traffic on the network, together with accident costs. An additional model calculates the time costs associated with breakdowns and accidents which occur in the work zone. Output available from the model includes information on the speed, queueing, and diversionary behaviour, of traffic in each hour of a typical week during the maintenance season, plus cost summaries by vehicle type and category.

There is a comprehensive manual procedure for work-zone evaluation adopted in the United States (11), which sets out a stage-by-stage process to permit the selection of the most appropriate traffic control strategy for a particular maintenance task. The method takes account of the items identified in the previous section III.5 and, combining local data with look-up tables and diagrams, allows costs to be assigned to the various elements. Some of the assessment elements are also available as routines on micro-computers. For example, estimations may be made of the additional user costs (time and vehicle operation) associated with simple lane closures using QUEWZ (Queue and User cost Evaluation at Work Zones) (14). An indication of the impact of traffic disruption due to maintenance projects may be obtained from another routine called CARHOP (Computer-Assisted Reconstruction -- Highway Operations and Planning) (15). This program provides a method of testing alternative maintenance management schemes by reviewing changes in journey time and travel on the surrounding network.

In Germany, whilst no generally applicable framework has been introduced to assess safety and traffic management aspects at work zones, many of the individual evaluation elements have been determined (3, 9, 16). For example, work zone speed/flow relationships have been established to enable speed changes to be determined (17), and hence the increases in time and vehicle operating costs to be assessed. In addition, surveys of accident data associated with differing traffic management layouts at work zones have helped to establish accident rates and costs for a wide range of circumstances and severities (18). The procedures for the full evaluation of a maintenance operation have also been determined. These consider both the implications of the works on users and the costs incurred by the construction agency

Figure III. 1

DEFINITION OF ACCIDENT RATES AT WORK ZONES
AS A FUNCTION OF SITE SUBDIVISIONS (QUADRO 2)

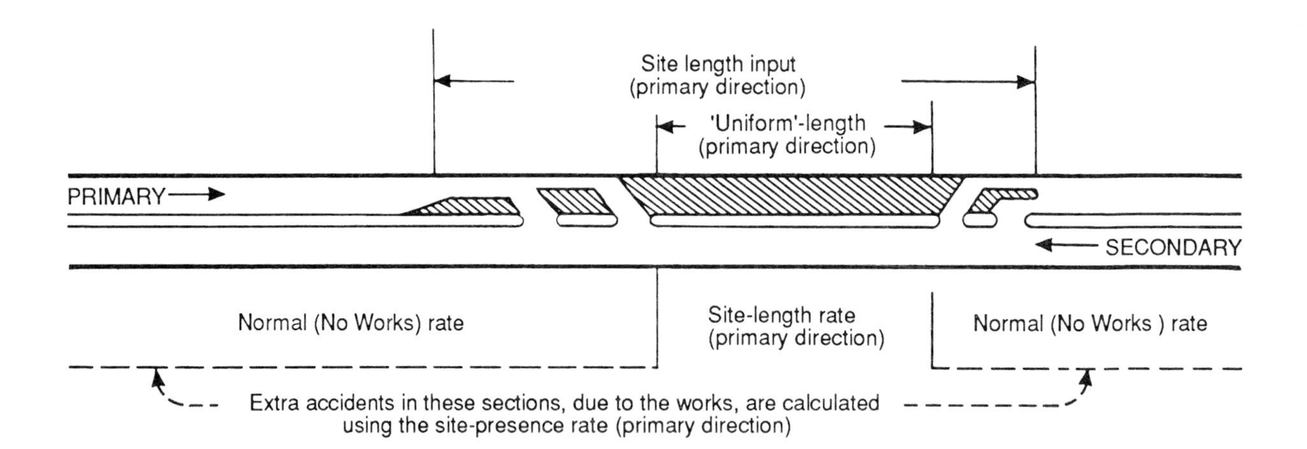

Table III.3

AVERAGE COST PER CASUALTY BY SEVERITY IN GERMANY, SWEDEN,
THE UNITED KINGDOM AND THE UNITED STATES (1986 LEVELS)

Casualty	Cost (DM)	Cost (SEK) (1)	Cost (£)	Cost ($)
Fatality	1220 000	4 200 000	480 000	1 500 000
Serious injury	55 000	600 000	14 025	39 000
Slight injury	44 700	40 000	290	12 000

1. These figures include all casualties, not only police-reported accidents. The police record all fatal accidents, and approximately 40-50 per cent of slight and serious injury accidents.

responsible for the project. The next stage is to utilise this framework and link together the individual cost relationships to form a comprehensive evaluation model.

III.7. DETERMINATION OF LONG-DURATION MAINTENANCE SCHEDULES

The national cost evaluation models presented before, are applied mainly to specific, individual maintenance projects scheduled in the near future. However, as hinted earlier, the principles they employ may be applied in the longer term to look at the economic consequences of different construction and maintenance decisions related to a length of road (or a network) over several years.

By combining the direct cost of the works and user cost relationships with models which can forecast the gradual deterioration of the pavement with traffic (or with time), investigations can be made of the economic implications of adopting alternative maintenance strategies (i.e. varying schedules and types of treatments).

III.7.1. Whole-life models

In addition to costs associated with the traffic user -- delays, vehicle operating costs and accidents -- other elements related more to the characteristics and nature of the pavement, need to be considered. These include:

-- The increase in travel time resulting from reduced speeds on poorly maintained sections;

-- Higher fuel consumption due to degraded surfaces;

-- Social and environmental issues (for example noise, both inside and outside the vehicle, due to poor surface characteristics);

-- The initial road construction cost;

-- Type of pavement (rigid or flexible);

-- The costs associated with the type of maintenance -- non-structural (resurfacing, etc.) and structural (overlaying, reconstruction, or any pavement strengthening tasks);

-- Budget constraints.

Several of these "whole-life" models, as they are known, have been developed, incorporating some of these concepts, but few are implemented at present.

The World Bank model, HDM3 (Highway Design and Maintenance Standards Model) is addressed to poorly maintained and lightly trafficked roads, whilst the American LCC2 (Life Cycle Costing Model), developed by the Pennsylvania

Department of Transportation is used to assess defined work schedules, rather than for longer term strategy determination.

In the United Kingdom, a model is being developed to estimate life-cycle costs of bituminous pavements and to study different maintenance profiles (19). By representing pavement deterioration under traffic, the model predicts when maintenance treatments will be needed, their cost and the delay costs to road users when works are in progress.

The total works and user costs, for a works' programme over the lifetime of the road, are then discounted to a base year. This enables maintenance tasks which occur in different years to be compared on a common basis. When comparing two maintenance life-cycle profiles, the economically preferred programme is the one with the lowest total discounted cost.

III.7.2. Penalties due to delayed maintenance

As might be expected, by adopting lower maintenance standards some reduction in the costs of maintenance work and traffic delays may be achieved. However, additional user costs are incurred, particularly when maintenance is deferred for extended periods. These result from increases in journey time, and fuel consumption and other vehicle operating costs, caused by the deterioration of the pavement surface.

The pavement surface irregularities (longitudinal and transverse) have a marked influence on driving comfort and safety of the users. A poor surface may exacerbate driver fatigue and will affect driving safety. Surface texture (influencing rolling resistance) and unevenness (inducing vibrations) affect fuel consumption.

Road and tyre noise are more noticeable when travelling on poor surfaces. This can become an important environmental consideration, since it has been noted that at speeds of over 50 km/h, the noise generated between tyre and road can account for up to 80 per cent of the vehicle noise (20).

Skid resistance is a major determinant of road user safety; a proper level of skid resistance will ensure good road-holding characteristics of vehicles, particularly on curves, and shorter braking distances. The planned introduction of a high standard of skid resistance surface for trunk roads (including motorways) in the United Kingdom, is expected to save up to 1 800 road-user casualties a year. The financial benefits from this forecast reduction in accidents on trunk roads will total about £35M per annum -- a return of £5.50 for every £1 spent.

Whilst all these effects per vehicle are small, when the total traffic is considered, these losses become significant. For example, it is estimated that if reconstruction was deferred on the trunk and motorway network in the United Kingdom, a cost penalty of about £15M per annum would be imposed on users. It can be seen therefore that good riding quality on roads is worthwhile not only for reasons of safety and comfort, but also for the possible additional benefits which may accrue from energy savings.

A cost benefit approach has not generally been regarded as an appropriate way to assess structural road maintenance. It is, however, possible to justify in cost-benefit terms the general principle of maintaining road structures. If roads are not maintained, they will eventually become unusable. Thus, it follows that the benefits from keeping a road open may be regarded as being basically the same as those from new road construction -- namely the saving of travel and accident costs. It costs significantly less to extend the life of a new road by maintenance, even if substantial or complete reconstruction is required, than it costs to construct a new road.

Given that road structures need to be maintained, the main economic question becomes not one of costs and benefits, but rather of how to minimise the cost of this necessary maintenance over the life of the road, while at the same time minimising the loss of user benefits due to the deterioration of road surface and the delays incurred during maintenance work.

It is hoped that by considering more fully the user costs and direct maintenance costs associated with such programmes, coupled with an understanding of pavement treatment and performance, this objective can be achieved.

III.8. CONCLUSIONS

Many countries have developed general road databases containing details of the level and composition of traffic flow. This primary network information, supplemented, on occasion, by detailed local data, is necessary for the traffic engineer, when planning maintenance programmes.

The continuing and increasing requirement for major road maintenance, coupled with limited public-sector resources, gives added impetus to the objective of achieving maximum value for money from this expenditure, in both works and user cost terms.

To assist in this aim, methods of economic appraisal have been developed, in some countries, for application both to specific schemes and to the evaluation of maintenance strategies over longer terms. However, these initial evaluation methods lack uniformity, and there is little compatibility between national costing procedures.

III.9. RECOMMENDATIONS

National road databases and local traffic records should be enhanced so that, for both major and minor works, a detailed comparison may be drawn between demand flow and work zone capacity to obtain an indication of the expected level of congestion.

Greater use should be made of cost evaluation procedures at work zones to determine more comprehensively the "true" (construction plus user) cost of maintenance, and to permit the effect of alternative maintenance programmes to be investigated at the planning stage.

The initial work zone evaluation procedures should be developed further, enhancing the costing methods as research in these areas expands, and updating the values of the models' parameters to ensure that the data remain current.

Closer links with pavement management systems should be initiated so as to bring together the traffic evaluation procedures associated with specific roadwork schemes and the predictive models for pavement performance. This would permit longer term evaluation of alternative strategies for the maintenance of a length of road.

A uniform approach should be developed when determining the evaluation elements (value of time, vehicle operating costs, etc) to ensure compatibility between national costing procedures.

REFERENCES

1. MELLORS, AR and QUEREE, C. The Department of Transport's Network Information System. Proceedings of PTRC Summer Meeting at Sussex University. Brighton, July 1985.

2. SWEDISH NATIONAL ROAD ADMINISTRATION. Road Data Bank. Swedish National Road Administration. Borlänge, 1979.

3. SCHMUCH, A and BECKER, H. Untersuchung über Einflüsse auf baustellenbedingte, geschwindigkeitsabhängige Anteile an den Strassennutzerkosten. Forschung Strassenbau und Strassenverkehrstechnik. Heft 421. Bundesminister für Verkehr (Herausgeber). Bonn, 1984.

4. MATHEWS, DH. Traffic Management for Major Roadworks on Dual Carriageways. Proceedings of PTRC Summer Meeting at Sussex University. Brighton, July 1984.

5. TRANSPORTATION RESEARCH BOARD. Highway Capacity Manual, Special Report 209. TRB, National Research Council. Washington, DC, 1985.

6. THE MVA CONSULTANCY, INSTITUTE FOR TRANSPORT STUDIES (LEEDS UNIVERSITY) AND TRANSPORT STUDIES UNIT (OXFORD UNIVERSITY). The Value of Travel Time Savings. (Report prepared for Department of Transport). Policy Journals. Newbury, 1987.

7. DEPARTMENT OF TRANSPORT. Values for Travel Time Savings and Accident Prevention. Department of Transport. London, 1987.

8. DIRECTION DES ROUTES, SERVICE D'ETUDES TECHNIQUES DES ROUTES ET AUTOROUTES. Instruction relative aux méthodes d'évaluation des investissements routiers en rase campagne. Ministère de l'Urbanisme, du Logement et des Transports. Paris, 1986.

9. FORSCHUNGSGESELLSCHAFT FUR STRASSEN- UND VERKEHRSWESEN: ARBEITSGRUPPE VERKEHRSPLANUNG. Richtlinien für die Anlage von Strassen RAS. Teil: Wirtschaftlichkeitsuntersuchungen RAS-W. Cologne, 1986.

10. DEPARTMENT OF TRANSPORT. COBA9 Manual. Department of Transport. London, 1981.

11. US DOT, FEDERAL HIGHWAY ADMINISTRATION. Planning and scheduling work zone traffic control. FHWA. Washington, DC, 1981.

12. SUMMERSGILL, I. Safety performance of traffic management at major roadworks on motorways in 1982. Department of Transport. Report RR42. Transport and Road Research Laboratory. Crowthorne, 1985.

13. DEPARTMENT OF TRANSPORT. QUADRO2 Manual. Department of Transport. London, 1981.

14. MEMMOTT, J and DUDEK, CL. Queue and user cost evaluation of work zones (QUEWZ). Transportation Research Record No. 979. Transportation Research Board. National Research Council. Washington, DC, 1984.

15. LEONARD, JD and RECKER, WW. CARHOP: An environment for computer assisted reconstruction -- highway operations and planning. University of California. Irvine, 1986.

16. FORSCHUNGSGESELLSCHAFT FUR STRASSEN- UND VERKEHRSWESEN. Arbeitspapier: Systematik der Strassenerhaltung, Wirtschaftlichkeitsuntersuchungen für Erhaltungsmassnahmen Ausserortsstrassen. 1987. (Unpublished).

17. BECKER, H and SCHMUCK, A. Verkehrsablauf an Autobahnbaustellen. Heft 14. Informationen -- Verkehrsplanung und Strassenwesen. Hochschule der Bundeswehr. Munich, 1983.

18. EMDE, W and HAMESTER, H. Unfallgeschehen an Autobahnbaustellen. Heft 14. Informationen -- Verkehrsplanung und Strassenwesen. Hochschule der Bundeswehr. Munich, 1983.

19. ABELL, R, STILL, PB and HARRISON, DA. Estimation of life cycle costs of pavements. Proceedings of the 1986 International Conference on Bearing Capacity of Roads and Airfields. Plymouth, September 1986.

20. OECD. ROAD TRANSPORT RESEARCH. Road surface characteristics: their interaction and their optimisation. OECD. Paris, 1984.

21. OECD. ROAD TRANSPORT RESEARCH. Pavement management systems. OECD, Paris, 1987.

Chapter IV

STRATEGIES

IV.1. FRAMEWORK

IV.1.1. Key issues

In order to respond to the increase in traffic and ensure good serviceability it is necessary to select the most appropriate strategies so as to minimise the effects of maintenance and rehabilitation works on safety and traffic flow.

In developing these strategies the main concerns are:

-- Programming of work zones in regard to both time and location;

-- Methods of planning and executing the construction work, as well as the role and tasks of management staff of both the authorities and the contractors;

-- Financing aspects;

-- Motorists' behaviour at work zones.

The principles are:

-- Work zones on roads under traffic and particularly motorways must be planned to take account of the traffic requirements;

-- The traffic management system and the organisation of construction work are closely connected. Measures taken in either of these sectors are interactive. They must be optimised by means of an iteration procedure;

-- Each measure for the benefit of safe and smooth traffic flow must be judged and assessed on the basis of the following questions:

  . Does this measure assure safety of the workers and high quality of work?

- Is the traffic improvement measure taken justifiable when compared to the costs involved?

- Can the negative effects of this measure -- induced temporary traffic disturbance compared with existing situation i.e. no repair works -- be accepted?

IV.1.2. Planning criteria

As a precondition for efficient and safe work planning and work site traffic regulations, precise knowledge of the following conditions is necessary (1):

-- Traffic: Traffic expected over the year, on weekdays, during 24 hours, during peak hours, proportion of heavy vehicle traffic, special traffic volumes, e.g. holiday traffic, speeds;

-- Work: Work to be carried out (type, amount, etc.), the sub-division into contract sections, frame conditions to ensure quality (temperature, weather, vibrations), possible methods of construction;

-- Locality: Work zone -- accessibility, property relationships, etc.;

Road area adjacent to the work zone -- geometry (number and proportioning of lanes, width of individual lanes, longitudinal and transverse gradients), structural design (pavements and their condition), traffic guidance devices, existing crossings of the central reservation etc;

Possibilities of bypassing the work zone locally by means of alternative routes;

-- Follow-up work: Work planned on the same road section or on the alternative route;

-- Environmental protection: Protection and protection of residents against nuisances, e.g. noise, exhaust gas.

IV.2. FINANCIAL ASPECTS

IV.2.1. Overall budget

There is a continuous need for maintenance activities to keep roads in safe and efficient conditions, both in regard to traffic operation and overall economy; to the extent possible serviceability levels and work productivity should be enhanced.

In Germany highway upkeep requirements for the federal trunk systems were determined under uniform criteria in accordance with a strategy model for the period from 1985 to 2000 (2). Additional investigations are currently carried out within the European Communities in order to identify the effects of higher vehicle weights and axle loads. Updating of the standard is planned as from 1990. The results will be included in financial planning and in the continuously updated five-year plans. A similiar strategy is followed in Sweden.

The United States is implementing a plan to preserve its highway system through resurfacing, restoring, rehabilitating and reconstructing its highways. Most of this work will be done while traffic is maintained.

In the United Kingdom the general procedure for the allocation of motorway and trunk road maintenance funds for expenditure is scheduled each year. There is no separate allocation of funds for the individual roadwork elements -- construction, road equipment, traffic management; a single sum of money is assigned to each scheme to cover the total cost.

IV.2.2. Bonus for reducing the works' duration

The work may be arranged so as to shorten to a maximum the overall construction time. Therefore, the possibility of extending work shifts should be adopted especially during the summer months. Daylight should, to the fullest extent possible, be used (3) and night work should not, as a rule, be excluded (1).

Moreover, as an incentive for shortening the duration of roadworks, contractors in Germany and in the United Kingdom can, at present, be granted a bonus for completion of works earlier than agreed. On the other hand, if the allocated period is exceeded the contractors will have to pay a penalty. This scheme -- the British version is known as "lane rental" -- has proved to be successful in both countries and is to be applied further. In Germany the acceptable "rent" to be paid per day and kilometre depends first of all on the traffic volume and thus on the extent of the disturbances prevented (see Table IV.1.). Incentive/penalty clauses are also being used in the United States. Costs are based on road user and/or inspection costs.

IV.3. TIME MANAGEMENT

IV.3.1. Principles

The following discussion refers to foreseeable construction works of longer duration on roads and motorways. Co-ordinating the planning and organisation of road construction projects over the network and by taking advantage of the seasonally differing traffic volumes, the financing and execution of such works can be arranged and timed in such a way that traffic disturbances are minimised.

If roadworks are nevertheless inevitable despite seasonally related high traffic loads, everything must be done to provide the required number of

Table IV.1.

BONUS PER DAY FOR EARLIER WORK COMPLETION (GERMANY)
IN DM/KM/DAY (1, 2)

	Traffic operation scheme (3)			
ADT (Veh./day)	2 + 2 (4) 3 + 1	4 + 0 3 + 2	2 + 1	2 + 0 1 + 1
< 20 000	600	800	2 300	2 800
20 000 - 30 000	1 000	1 400	-	-
30 000 - 40 000	1 500	2 200	-	-
40 000 - 50 000	2 100	3 200	-	-
50 000 - 60 000	2 900	4 200	-	-
> 60 000	3 600	5 200	-	-

(1) The quotation for "km" is the length of the speed limit < 80 km/h due to the work zone.

(2) "Day" is every calendar-day with undisturbed traffic resulting from the shortened construction time.

(3) Only speed limit < 80 km/h;

(4) If the speed limit is valid only for one carriageway in one direction the values must be halved.

lanes in the work zone in order to maintain smooth flow of traffic. If necessary, the shifting of lanes, the narrowing of lanes (temporary lanes) and special construction measures must be accepted. If these measures are not sufficient alternative routes should be provided. In the last resort the number of lanes is to be reduced. For peak traffic loads of 1 200 motor vehicles per hour or more in each direction two temporary lanes should be made available for each direction (1, 3).

IV.3.2. Timing of work zone activities

In most of the countries which have to cope with high traffic volumes, roadworks are, if possible, not carried out during those times of the year when traffic peaks are expected. These are mainly periods of tourist holidays where work on the most important and highly trafficked roads is either totally stopped or at least reduced. Work should be postponed to seasons with lower traffic loads. However, works could be carried out on roads with lower traffic volumes during the main travel seasons, thus contributing to a better utilisation of the capacities of the construction industry.

On the basis of an analysis and evaluation of data recorded by traffic counters, it is now possible to determine critical traffic volumes and provide useful graphic -- hourly, daily, weekly etc. -- displays. Road traffic census are now mostly performed on motorways and possibly the primary road network, graphic displays can help to determine the best time for setting up a work zone.

IV.3.3. Night work

With increasing traffic volumes on urban motorways, it becomes more difficult to perform maintenance and reconstruction work without causing major traffic delays and safety problems. One alternative is in principle to perform the needed roadway work at night, but there are many potential disadvantages which must be taken into consideration.

In many countries night and shift activities are not generally recommended and in principle not to be prescribed except in an emergency, such as removal of damaged vehicles or restoration of safety. However, discussions about using night work for shortening the duration of the work zone are bound to be more and more frequent.

As regards winter maintenance activities (17), these are increasingly carried out in the early morning and during the night so that they will be finished before the commuter traffic starts. In the larger cities some of the road markings or maintenance tasks are performed at night.

On some congested urban motorways night-time working is becoming common as more lane rental schemes (see section IV.2.2) are introduced. The main criticism is the additional pressure which this shift working puts on staff, but the authorities can assign extra staff to ensure the hours worked are kept to a reasonable level. According to the assessment of the contractors their efficiency had improved within their own organisation especially in regard to resource planning and the use of higher output machinery.

Night-time work activity, apart from possible environmental problems in urban areas, does allow maintenance to be performed on many busy sections of the network, with a minimum of user inconvenience. It may also represent the only period when closures can be established safely if daytime traffic volumes are high.

Layout changes are also planned to coincide with the night-time period of low traffic flow. This includes the extension of the traffic management scheme further along the carriageway in preparation for the next phase of the works, or the closure of additional lanes -- overnight -- to increase the works area for plant and materials.

In the United States discussions about night work zone activities are also going on. The key consideration is the degree of congestion or vehicle delay caused by daytime lane closures. Although some agencies accept long delays as being a part of daytime road work, others do not and opt for night work, even though working at night is usually considered the least attractive alternative. Because of the increased emphasis on maintenance and rehabilitation of existing facilities, coupled with the high traffic volumes in urban areas, there is reason to believe that more night operations will have to be scheduled (4).

The main advantages of night work are:

-- Less congestion and delay for users;

-- Opportunity to enlarge work zones and to conduct multiple work functions at the same time;

-- Longer, safer and more productive working hours with less interruption, less traffic interference and at more moderate temperatures;

-- Use of the full capacity of production plants, and more efficient hauling because of less congestion and better access;

-- Shorter set-up time.

Disadvantages of night work zone activities are:

-- Night traffic can be more dangerous because of higher speeds and more prevalent driver intoxication (alcohol, drugs) and inattentiveness, together with unexpected conditions with restricted visibility;

-- Lower visibility for the working staff, even with supplementary lighting, especially for tasks requiring accurate depth perception;

-- Adverse public reaction to noise in residential areas;

-- Personnel problems: difficulties in recruiting or becoming accustomed to night work, more employees working two jobs;

-- Difficulty in repairing equipment breakdowns;

-- Problems in obtaining materials if plants do not remain open, or in obtaining service from utilities;

-- Lower quality workmanship, especially if there is pressure to ensure completion of job or to have road open prior to morning rush period;

-- Higher cost because of pay increase, material acquisition, increased traffic control, lighting, etc.

Although there are many potential disadvantages of working at night, it is believed that through the experience that has been gained and proper planning, the night alternative is feasible for selected work. Night work is less an operational problem but more an institutional problem.

IV.3.4. Planning of work zones

The planning of work zones in the network is closely connected to their timing. The objective is to ensure as much as possible the function and the capacity of longer road sections despite the work activity. Roadworks should not be carried out at the same time on parallel alternative routes. Equally, no roadworks should be started during the tourist and main travel seasons at substitute routes in the vicinity of motorway sites.

IV.4. CO-ORDINATED PLANNING AND WORK IMPLEMENTATION

IV.4.1. Guidelines

Guidelines are issued to minimise the impairment of traffic flow and safety, which may occur during maintenance activities in particular when carrying out maintenance and rehabilitation work on highways and especially on roads for long-distance traffic. They include the following measures:

-- Shortening of construction times, especially on motorways with high traffic volumes;

-- A better balanced arrangement and timing of work zones, thus avoiding a concentration of work zones;

-- Reduction of the number of work zones during holiday periods.

For example in Germany, guidelines for the planning and execution of construction work on federal motorways (3) are applied to all work zones which occupy the carriageway and last for more than two weeks. The road authorities have to set up route-related plans valid for one year and submit them at the beginning of each year to the Ministry of Transport for approval, so that the planner can judge if the disturbances are acceptable. The plans contain information on:

-- The conditions of the route:

. Number of lanes;
. Location of interchanges, entries and exits;
. Kilometrage;
. Gradient, if more than 4%;

-- The planned construction work:

. Location;
. Type of work;
. Construction time, holiday periods, days without work restrictions;
. Traffic management systems during the individual stages of construction;
. Speed restrictions;
. Possible use of auxiliary lanes;
. Complete or partial blocking of the carriageways.

Maps showing traffic volumes are also used for the assessment of the plans.

The press is given a map of the motorway network each year for publication showing the work zones in operation during the main holiday season (June to September).

The construction schedule also contains basic data for the holiday traffic forecast published each year by the Ministry of Transport (5). In order to reduce congestion, delays and accidents, this forecast advises holiday makers as well as all other motorists travelling on the motorways to avoid the indicated bottlenecks by the careful selection of their departure time and appropriate route.

Similar provisions have been introduced in most reporting countries, taking into account their specific organisational structures, where traffic peaks occur on motorways and other highways at certain times.

For example in the United Kingdom, meetings are held each year between the Department of Transport, local authorities and the police, in order to co-ordinate the planned maintenance work on those motorways which carry a particularly high level of traffic, so that the effects of the construction work on traffic are kept as low as possible.

In France, an operational study is prepared for each intended work zone on the autoroute, which results in a description of the project. The Road Information Center is informed of the beginning and end of the work and of changes in the traffic management, and can thus act accordingly and instruct road users.

In addition, annual discussions are held in the spring in Europe to ensure co-ordination of major works at an international level.

IV.4.2. Length of work zones

On motorways or dual carriageways the length of work zones with narrowed lanes, i.e. with limited capacity, are generally restricted so as to be acceptable by motorists.

The length can vary from 4 to 15 km (or more without narrowed lanes), according to specific conditions (e.g. contra-flow). The connection between lane width and the length of the work zone must not be ignored, and is developed in Chapter V.

IV.4.3. Minimum distances between consecutive work zones

The minimum distances between consecutive work zones should be such that the flow of traffic can return to normal between them. The separation should permit fast-moving traffic to overtake slow-moving vehicles so that platoons can be dissipated and traffic normalised (4).

These distances could vary from 2 km on urban roads (50 km/h), to 5 or 10 km generally prescribed on rural roads or motorways, or more according to gradients, traffic levels or traffic operation scheme (contra-flow for example).

IV.5. RESPONSIBILITIES AND CONTRACTS

IV.5.1. Preliminary studies

As a rule, during the preparation of competitive tendering for road works and above all before awarding a contract, the legitimate interests of all those affected by the measure must be taken into consideration. Those concerned are in general:

-- The motorists;

-- The general public, business, residents;

-- The firms competing for the construction contract;

-- The administrative authorities (construction authorities and transport authorities including traffic police).

Tenders should only be invited if all contract documents have been completed by the highway administration and if the work can start within the time indicated. The formulation of the project specifications is among the most important preparatory works of the authorities. This specification is the result of comprehensive co-ordination and planning which must also include the development of optimum traffic engineering solutions taking into consideration the following criteria:

-- Safety for workers and motorists;

-- Quality requirements, e.g. efficient traffic management systems;

-- Economic efficiency;

-- Time frame;

-- Environmental impact.

Figure IV.1 gives a rough outline of a possible plan.

In the case of large-scale and complex work projects where the aforementioned requirements cannot be complied with during the routine procedure, additional special consultations with the competent authorities are necessary, for example if:

-- The use of new techniques which have not been tested recently, is needed;

-- The construction project can only be realised in stages and with changing traffic operation systems resulting in capacity restrictions;

-- The project entails exceptional risks regarding safety and financial requirements;

-- The time allocated to the construction work is oriented at certain constraints, e.g. traffic peaks during the holiday season, and if the work cannot be delayed.

These considerations are to minimize the risks for all those affected by the construction measure before the beginning of the work activities.

IV.5.2. Responsibilities and traffic control plans (TCP)

Road traffic and highway construction authorities as well as the contractor have to harmonize their activities, required for securing work zones, before the beginning of the roadwork. Special plans are prepared before the tendering; they contain information about traffic signing and traffic management systems.

Figure IV. I OUTLINE OF POSSIBLE PLANNING APPROACH

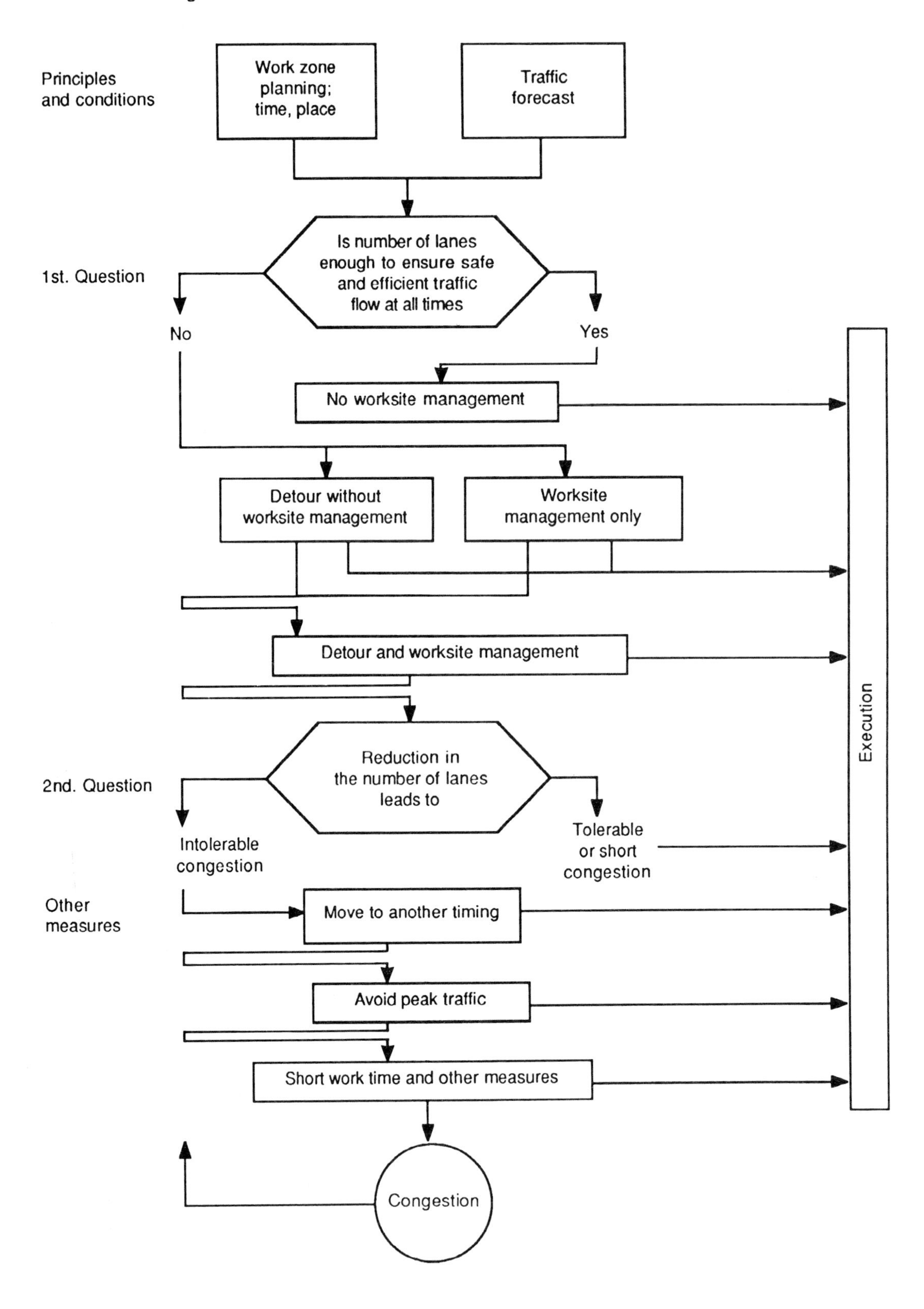

Before starting the construction work, which will influence traffic, the contractor has to get the legal permission of the road traffic authority about the means and extent of securing the work zone. The proposal -- including a traffic control plan (TCP) -- based on examples stated in special guidelines (6), should contain the following specifications:

-- Size of the work zone;

-- Kind of traffic disturbances;

-- Beginning of the work and prospective duration;

-- Existing and additional markings, traffic signs and devices;

-- Possible diversion routes;

-- Lighting;

-- Traffic signs, which can change from day to night; and

-- Description of alternative traffic signal systems;

-- Responsible person for the correct setup of the equipment.

As a rule, in Germany for example, these proposals are presented by the contractor and checked by the construction authorities and, in special cases, by the traffic authorities and the traffic police. If they agree, the TCP is to be used by the contractor. Traffic authorities, construction authorities and the police have to control the regulation of traffic following the TCP. The contractor is responsible for the visibility of the traffic signs and the traffic installations during the duration of the work zone. The equipment has to be cleaned regularly.

In general the signals are inspected daily, either by an Administration supervisor or by an agent of the contractor, who submits an inspection report to the Administration. The contractor is required to restore signals without delay and he can be penalised if he ignores the injunctions.

In Belgium a fine of up to BFr. 5 000 may occur if damaged signals are not replaced within 30 minutes and BFr. 10 000 for every further 30 minute delay. It is therefore a requirement that standby traffic signal equipment be available on site. If a contractor fails to meet his obligations the Administration may file a complaint and, if necessary, take action on its own initiative, doing the contractor's job by replacing signals or having them replaced without waiting for the liability to be allocated.

In Sweden, the road supervisor has the responsibility for all activities on the road network. If something happens to a road user and a contractor is involved, the Swedish National Road Administration will solve the problem together with the road user. Then the administration will take up discussions with the contractor in order to reach an agreement with him. To point out the importance of proper signing, the name of the person who is in charge of signing and signalling at the work zone must be written in the contract. This person shall continuously keep in touch with the road supervisor.

In the United States, the plan for handling traffic, including the traffic signal plan (TSP), is the traffic control plan (TCP) (see Annex B).

IV.6. TRAFFIC MANAGEMENT

IV.6.1. Objectives and factors

Handling traffic in work zones is challenging, because work activities present abnormal and often disruptive elements to motorists and pedestrians. The objectives of work zone traffic management are to provide safe and expeditious movement of traffic while the work progresses as rapidly, safely and efficiently as possible.

Traffic management strategies to be used at work zones must include the following fundamental principles:

-- Make traffic safety an integral and high priority element of every project;

-- Avoid inhibiting traffic as much as possible;

-- Guide motorists in a clear and positive way;

-- Perform routine inspection of traffic control elements and traffic operations;

-- Give constant attention to roadside safety.

As a matter of fact there are no universally applicable procedures for traffic management at highway work zones: each specific case has a unique solution. Regulations should be considered as guidelines instead of standard procedures. Nevertheless, certain solutions have common traits influenced by factors such as:

-- Environment: rural, urban;

-- Type of highway:

. 2-way, 2-lanes or more;
. 4- or 6-lanes undivided;
. Divided carriageways or motorways (2- or 3-lanes);

-- Traffic volume and speed, both upstream and at the work area, with and without work in progress;

-- Type of traffic: mixed (including heavy freight vehicles) or segregated (passenger cars only), even temporarily;

-- Available sight distance upstream and at the work zone;

-- Mobility of work zone, when not stationary. In moving operations such as whitelining, weedspraying, deflectograph surveying, etc. workers and equipment move along the road without stopping, usually at slow speed. In mobile operations such as pothole patching or debris collection frequent short stops are made, up to 15 minutes;

-- Transversal encroachment of work zone compared with normal platform:

- External or median;
- Shoulders (inner or outer);
- Carriageway (with closure of no lane, one lane or more lanes) kept open to traffic;
- Total closure of one or both carriageways;

-- Duration of work, especially if prolonged through the night or weekends. Short-duration work is usually defined as taking less than one period of daylight and not being performed at night; worker exposure to traffic should be reduced as much as possible by getting the work done quickly and avoiding peak periods of traffic. Problems specific to short-duration operations are discussed in more detail in Chapter V;

-- Danger involved in case of intrusion into work zone.

IV.6.2. Influence on traffic conditions

Hindrance to traffic may arise from speed reduction and/or reduction in the number of lanes. Some degree of compromise between safety and capacity has to be reached. Should the latter become insufficient, safety problems can arise upstream of the work zone because of congestion. In the United States on divided highways, work zones which restrict capacity should not exceed 6 km in length (see also Section IV.4.2 and Chapter V). The obvious first choice is not to reduce the number of lanes.

To minimise the extent of the disruption to traffic, the work zone should be kept as small as possible; however, traffic management measures for adjacent small projects are usually encompassed into a single, larger zone, thus reducing conflict points and decisions for the motorist.

The whole management system (complemented by signs, delineation and, if necessary, barriers) must be designed to meet the motorists' limitations and minimise the demands of the driving task; it should be easily read by an average driver who, perhaps unattentive or unskilled, should not be confronted with unexpected or difficult-to-understand situations, his/her reaction to which could lead to an accident. Therefore the system should:

-- Help drivers to make proper choices rapidly:

- Identify and minimise the number of alternatives;
- Give adequate warning times and allow time for an appropriate choice to be made;
- Separate decision points;
- Provide pertinent information only;
- Do not assume that users will see or recognize workers or hazards in the work area;

-- Reinforce critical information without being excessive:

- Assure that if information is missed in one form, it can be received in another form;
- Increase the percentage of drivers who understand the information;
- Reduce the potential for ambiguity;
- Avoid distracting drivers from important information through oversigning;

-- Appear credible and override conflicting information:

- Uniformity in strategies, signing and spacing;
- No unnecessarily restrictive speed limits;
- No warning to expect hazards that are not there;
- Cover or removal of unapplicable signs;

-- Follow the evolution of the works both in time and space, and be removed as soon as it becomes partially or totally unnecessary.

The separation of decision points for the driver is important. As far as possible, measures should be taken one at a time, for instance lane closures should not be made at the same place where speed is reduced. Uniformity is also an important aspect of safety.

Different areas have to be studied as shown in the typical sequence of Figure IV.2.

Traffic management in short-term, mobile and moving operations is more critical, because these operations are usually not set-up with formal traffic control plans, and many decisions must be taken on-the-spot.

IV.6.3. Traffic operation

In order to minimise these drawbacks the traffic manager should choose the safest and most efficient operation, as developed in Chapter V, to have clear, separated zones under circulation and for works:

-- Maintaining the number of lanes, with altered layout and/or narrow lanes, contra-flow or added lanes, so that the traffic flow (one-way) does not exceed 1 300 to 1 400 veh/h/lane;

-- Closing lanes as little as possible with reversible lanes if necessary, but leaving at least one lane open in each direction. Traffic demand should not exceed 1 100 to 1 200 veh/h/lane on undivided highways, or 1 400 to 1 600 veh/h/lane with segregated flow on divided carriageways (cf. Chapter III, Table III.1);

-- Using one-way operations with fixed priority, agents or signals if short work zone length and low traffic volumes allow it;

-- Finding some limited extra-capacity with diversions to alternative routes if they can support it and if they are carefully controlled.

Figure IV. 2 AREAS IN A TRAFFIC CONTROL ZONE

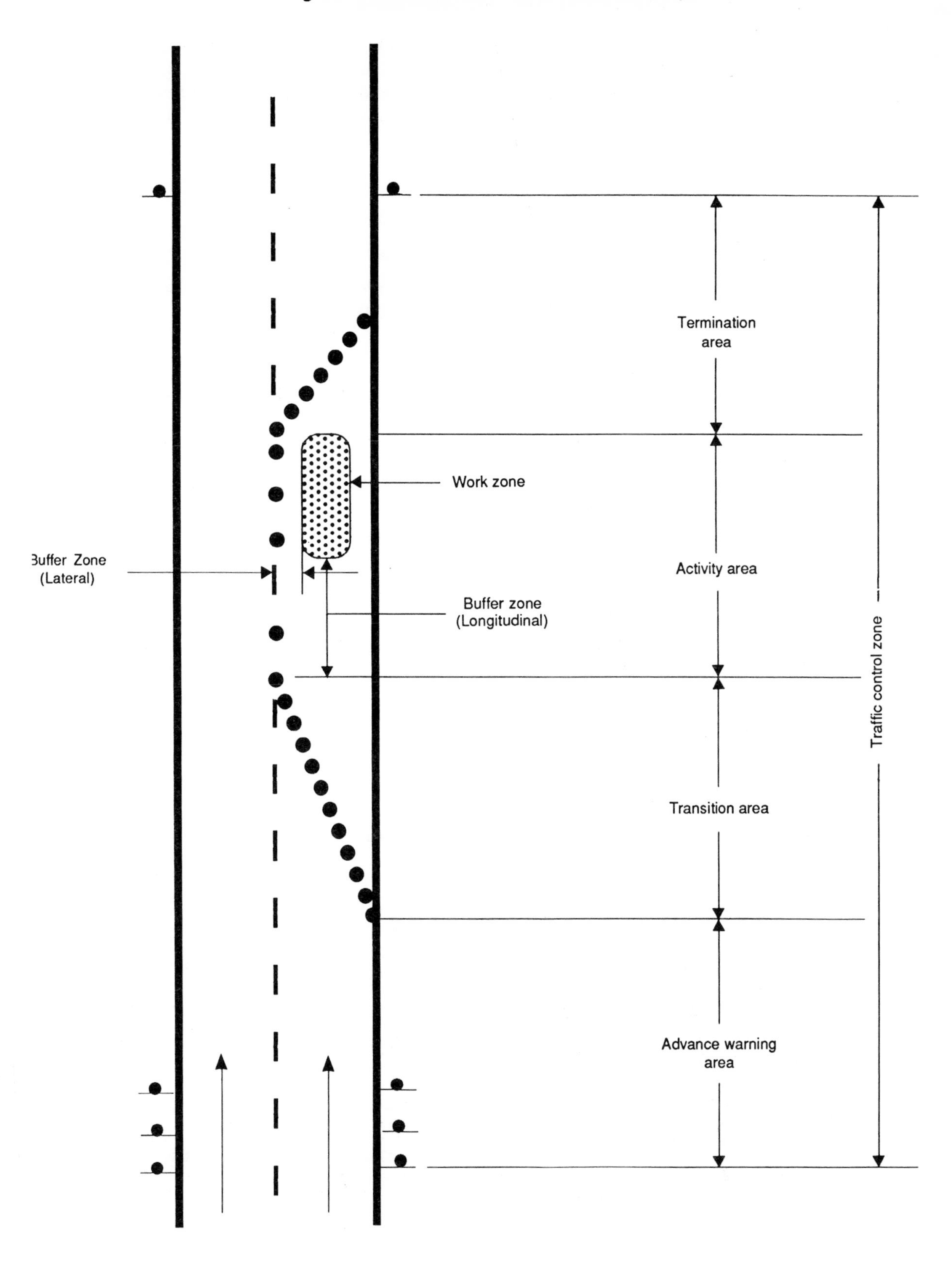

IV.6.4. Policing of work zone traffic management

To ensure that the traffic management layout at a work zone is operating both safely and effectively as planned it should be inspected and evaluated immediately after it becomes operational, and then routinely throughout the life of the project. During inspections the following should be examined:

- -- Adherence to the original plan;
- -- Condition (day and night) of traffic management devices;
- -- Adaptation to changed field conditions;
- -- Location of accidents and incidents which may assist in identifying the areas where layout-modifications maybe required.

IV.7. TRAINING AND INFORMATION

IV.7.1. Human factors

In all traffic management aspects (safety, congestion, comfort) the human factors are of first importance. To understand phenomena and develop adapted systems and actions, it is a priority to pay great attention to all comments, proposals and/or complaints put forward by road users and workers.

Studies in Sweden and in the United States clearly show increasing nervous stress and difficulties especially for agents concerned with motorways work activities.

IV.7.2. Training of work zone personnel

Providing traffic controls for work zone operations is complex and it is becoming more difficult to perform them safely and efficiently because more work is being done under traffic.

Safety in work zones cannot be achieved only by traffic-related means (traffic signs, traffic installations, warning and protective installations and provisions relating to traffic law). It depends on each person involved in the process from the initial planning to the installation and monitoring of the controls on the highway. The behaviour of the agency staff, the personnel of the contractor as well as the traffic police, with all their human shortcomings, must also be the target of the efforts for safety enhancement.

Education and training programmes are developed in most countries by the Administration or by professional associations. Handbooks, audio-visuals, practical training courses and special exercise materials are prepared for managers and road workers. The topics include legal aspects as well as examples of correct application of current maintenance techniques in a safe and efficient manner, as well as new methods of road operation. The course material could include, for example, the use of traffic signs and other devices, or closing of a road or part of it to traffic and how this can best be achieved.

These training courses often cover all levels of staff and deal with topics as varied as financial management, contract law and road maintenance. In some countries, the United States for example, training is required for all persons from government agencies or contractors and companies. All these documents (general reports, standards for equipment and signing, guidelines, handbooks, etc.) are of great importance for the observance of safety and of traffic requirements. They constitute an essential working basis for those people involved, not only to solve technical problems but also to regulate responsibilities. Their contents, e.g. their text and figures, should be as clear and simple as possible (6, 8, 9, 10, 11).

In order to maintain the benefits of existing provisions and to enhance them they must be permanently updated. This requires an adaptation to the latest state of technology, and an exchange of experiences between the authorities, the industries and all people concerned with the work zones.

IV.7.3. Information to drivers

Proper motorist behaviour in road traffic can, as a rule, be achieved by two methods which are complementary:

-- By means of legal instructions, adapted to the situation in the form of traffic signs before and in work zones in conjunction with traffic police surveillance; and

-- Within the framework of general information on the traffic situation by advising motorists of the work zones and their effects on traffic while at the same time giving recommendations to minimise disadvantages.

The methods used by the individual reporting countries for motorist information at work zones are different. Conventional methods -- which can, however, still be improved -- are:

-- Traffic advice in the local press;
-- Variable message signs with advice in real time;
-- Local radio broadcasts during normal radio programmes;
-- Calls to information centers, radio stations or automobile associations.

The road traffic information to be broadcast includes the impacts of work zones. It can be improved by being more accessible, timely and place specific. Efforts are already being made in some countries to use the Radio-Data-System (RDS) and the Traffic-Message-Channel (TMC). Encoded road traffic information transmitted by RDS can be stored in the receiver and can, as required, be output at any time in any desired language or script. These systems as well as the new in-car communication techniques could offer route guidance for drivers.

The information given via screen display may be improved with modern telecommunication services such as: Teletext and Viewdata system. These are increasingly being offered where the information can be called at any time or where it is repeated at regular intervals (7). Information terminals can be installed at filling stations and service areas as well as at important parking areas.

A decisive factor for the quality of the information is the technique and the organisation of a pertinent reporting system. Reports on the basis of data are transmitted:

-- By the traffic police concerning the traffic situation;

-- By the public and private organisations responsible for the traffic, and particularly for the construction and operation on work zones whose size, duration and impact on the traffic flow necessitate the most widespread information.

These reports are prepared in regional centres which are interconnected and passed on to the media for transmission. In some countries the news transfer has already been automated by means of electronic data processing.

For the effective dissemination of useful and comprehensive information on road traffic situations including work zones, close co-ordination with the media is required in order to allocate sufficient space or broadcasting time.

On high-capacity motorways and in large cities, the practice of distributing leaflets to motorists is increasingly applied informing them early about the reasons for the construction work and its duration as well as giving recommendations on how to minimise the traffic obstruction (France, Sweden, United Kingdom, United States), or bypass the work zone (Annex C).

In 1986, the Dutch Road Administration together with other parties concerned such as the Dutch Association of Road Constructors started a special public relations and advertising campaign for better mutual understanding between workers and users. In this context, the motorist was regularly advised about safer driving behaviour when approaching and passing work zone. In order to reach the best possible results, the campaign was developed with the assistance of professional public relations and advertising companies.

This type of campaign leads to positive results concerning modified driving behaviour or a more positive attitude of the motorist towards the "men on the road". It also concerns workers motivation in terms of more attention to traffic safety and more interest in an uninterrupted traffic flow.

In the United States, several states have initiated similar campaigns to make the public more aware of the hazards associated with driving through work zones. Some states have used radio and television public service announcements and distributed printed material to alert drivers of the need for increased caution to safely negotiate highway work areas. At least one state has formed a special committee charged with updating driver education courses to include a special section on driving in work zones.

In Japan, around OSAKA, the HANSHIM Toll Expressway Public Corporation, initiated a new extreme strategy: work activities are carried out under totally suspended traffic on the loop line. Due to the increase of both traffic volume and repair works, it was not possible to avoid congestions even on holidays. Instead of more than 70 days work under regulated traffic, it was proposed in 1988 six days uninterrupted work of all kinds, for the Southward loop line and five days for the Northward with no traffic on these tunnels. It was successfully achieved thanks to a very large campaign of public relations and road users' information through all media and large cooperation with all public and private organisations.

On individual projects, multi-dimensional public information systems have been established as a source of information on lane closures, major shifts in work zone traffic patterns, alternate routes and alternate mode of transport. These include:

-- Public information office;

-- Advisory committee;

-- Community Involvement Program Office where the public can visit and obtain first-hand information;

-- Direct mailings to residents;

-- Billboard signing;

-- Maps and project information brochures;

-- TV and radio public service announcements and reports;

-- Newspaper advertising and special articles;

-- News releases;

-- Hotline telephone operators and recorded messages;

-- Public information meetings;

-- Models of project for public viewing.

IV.8. CONCLUSIONS

The following are the major findings of this Chapter's review:

-- The main purpose of an adequate strategy is to examine the totality of traffic management at all the steps of roadworks from the design of the project to the monitoring of the operation and post-evaluation.

-- Planning and co-ordination have to be optimised and specified for the tender in regard to technical and economic aspects (e.g. Traffic Control Plan). Sufficient financial planning has to secure the execution of the necessary maintenance and rehabilitation.

-- The responsibilities of each individual concerned with the traffic management should be clearly defined.

-- Time organisation is fundamental to choose the off-peak period and to reduce the duration, especially on motorways work zones.

-- Such a shortening of the work activities duration can be achieved by the use of innovative procedures, techniques and equipment. This may at first increase the cost of the work, but as it improves safety, it would decrease the cost of accidents and of travel time for users.

-- Night works are increasing in most congested urban areas, and ask for specific procedures, social acceptance and financial arrangements.

-- Space co-ordination, length and intervals between work zones, must be carefully controlled to avoid the accumulation of hindrances on the main or alternative routes.

-- Narrow lanes or altered layout should be used as far as possible to avoid flow restrictions and one-way or diversion shortcomings.

-- In all cases the layout has to be clear and simple for the drivers, and well adapted to each step of the situation.

-- Workers' education and drivers' information are necessary for behaviour improvements in safety or regulatory aspects, and in order to set comprehensive strategies.

IV.9 RECOMMENDATIONS

The major proposals are to:

-- Generalise preliminary studies and contract specifications for a well adapted and co-ordinated traffic management programme.

-- Perform adequate financial planning according to the road upkeep requirements.

-- Proceed with experiments to optimise and harmonize control strategies such as narrow lane, contra-flow, reversible lanes, etc.

-- Develop traffic monitoring methods so as to forecast and adapt strategies to real conditions.

-- Organise education and information systems to assure better understanding by and behaviour of drivers and workers.

REFERENCES

1. ASSOCIATION OF ENGINEERS RAPP. Engineers + planners, Basle. Measures for the maintenance of traffic in work zones on motorways and roads. Edition April 1987. Basel/Neuchatel, 1987.

2. DER BUNDESMINISTER FÜR VERKEHR. Bund/Laender-Arbeitsgruppe. Schlussbericht "Ermittlung des Erhaltungsbedarfs für Bundesfernstrassen". Bonn, May 1985.

3. DER BUNDESMINISTER FÜR VERKEHR. Richtlinien für die Planung und Durchführung von Bauarbeiten an Betriebsstrecken der Bundesautobahnen. Bonn, December 1977.

4. US DOT, FEDERAL HIGHWAY ADMINISTRATION. Benefits and safety impacts of night work-zone activities. Report No. FHWA/RD-85/067. FHWA. Washington DC, June 1985.

5. DER BUNDESMINISTER FÜR VERKEHR. Ferienverkehrsprognose 1987. Informationen zum Urlaubsreiseverkehr. Bonn, 1987.

6. DER BUNDESMINISTER FÜR VERKEHR. Richtlinien für die Sicherung von Arbeitsstellen an Strassen (RSA) Stand 1986. Verkehrsblatt-Verlag.

7. ABERDING, M, SCHNEIDER HW and ZINN, H. Moderne Telekommunikations-technologien für integrierte Strassenverkehrsinformationsdienste. Forschungsarbeit im Auftrag des Bundesministers für Forschung und Technologie. April 1987.

8. US DOT, FEDERAL HIGHWAY ADMINISTRATION. Manual on uniform traffic control devices (MUTCD). By the American National Standard Institute. FHWA. Washington, DC, 1971

9. US DOT, FEDERAL HIGHWAY ADMINISTRATION. Traffic Control Devices Handbook (TCDH). FHWA. Washington, DC, 1983.

10. US DOT, FEDERAL HIGHWAY ADMINISTRATION. Work Zone Traffic Control - Standards and Guidelines. FHWA. Washington, DC, 1985.

11. US DOT, FEDERAL HIGHWAY ADMINISTRATION. National Highway Institute. Design and Operation of Work Zone Traffic Control. (Participant Note Book.) FHWA. Washington, DC, 1987.

12. OECD. ROAD RESEARCH. Traffic operation at sites of temporary obstruction. OECD. Paris, February 1973.

13. MINISTERE DE L'URBANISME, DU LOGEMENT ET DES TRANSPORTS. SETRA. Instruction relative aux méthodes d'évaluation des investissements routiers en rase campagne/en milieu urbain. SETRA. Paris, 1986.

14. MINISTERE DE L'URBANISME, DU LOGEMENT ET DES TRANSPORTS. SETRA. Exploitation sous chantier -- clauses types à inclure dans les documents contractuels. SETRA. Paris, 1978

15. MINISTERE DE L'URBANISME, DU LOGEMENT ET DES TRANSPORTS. SETRA. Exploitation sous chantier -- dossiers pilotes du Directeur de Travaux et de la cellule d'exploitation et de sécurité routière. SETRA. Paris, 1978

16. MINISTERE DE L'URBANISME, DU LOGEMENT ET DES TRANSPORTS. SETRA. Les Prévisions "Bison Futé" sur les difficultés de circulation. Note d'information N° 43. SETRA. Paris, May 1987.

17. OECD. ROAD TRANSPORT RESEARCH. Curtailing usage of de-icing agents in winter maintenance. GECD. Paris, 1989.

Chapter V

TRAFFIC MANAGEMENT TECHNIQUES

V.1. INTRODUCTION

Work zone traffic control covers four areas: the advance warning, the transition, the activity (buffer and work) and the termination sections, and involves the use of some of the following managerial and guidance techniques (Figure V.1):

- -- Lane (or shoulder) closure;
- -- Total or partial diversion: detours, contra-flow;
- -- Speed control (up to complete stop);
- -- Prohibition of overtaking manoeuvres;
- -- Lane alteration: narrow lanes, altered layout, added lanes;
- -- One-way operation: shuttle operation, reversible lanes.

Because of the varying prevailing circumstances, proper monitoring is required and modifications of traffic control devices may be necessary.

Most ordinary maintenance and public utility operations carried out in the road space, are of short duration or mobile. Because of their dynamic and temporary nature, traffic management may therefore vary from that used for relatively long-duration work activities (1).

V.2. LANE CLOSURE

V.2.1. Situations

In most cases, work on existing routes encroaches on the running lanes and shoulders and therefore represents a hindrance to normal traffic flow. Reduction of the number of lanes is a possible policy but its consequences on the level of service, especially if resulting in delays and/or congestion, should always be evaluated; any alternative strategy would in principle be preferable to a reduction in the number of lanes (see sub-section IV.6.3.).

Figure V. 1 LANE ALTERATION ON WORK ZONES

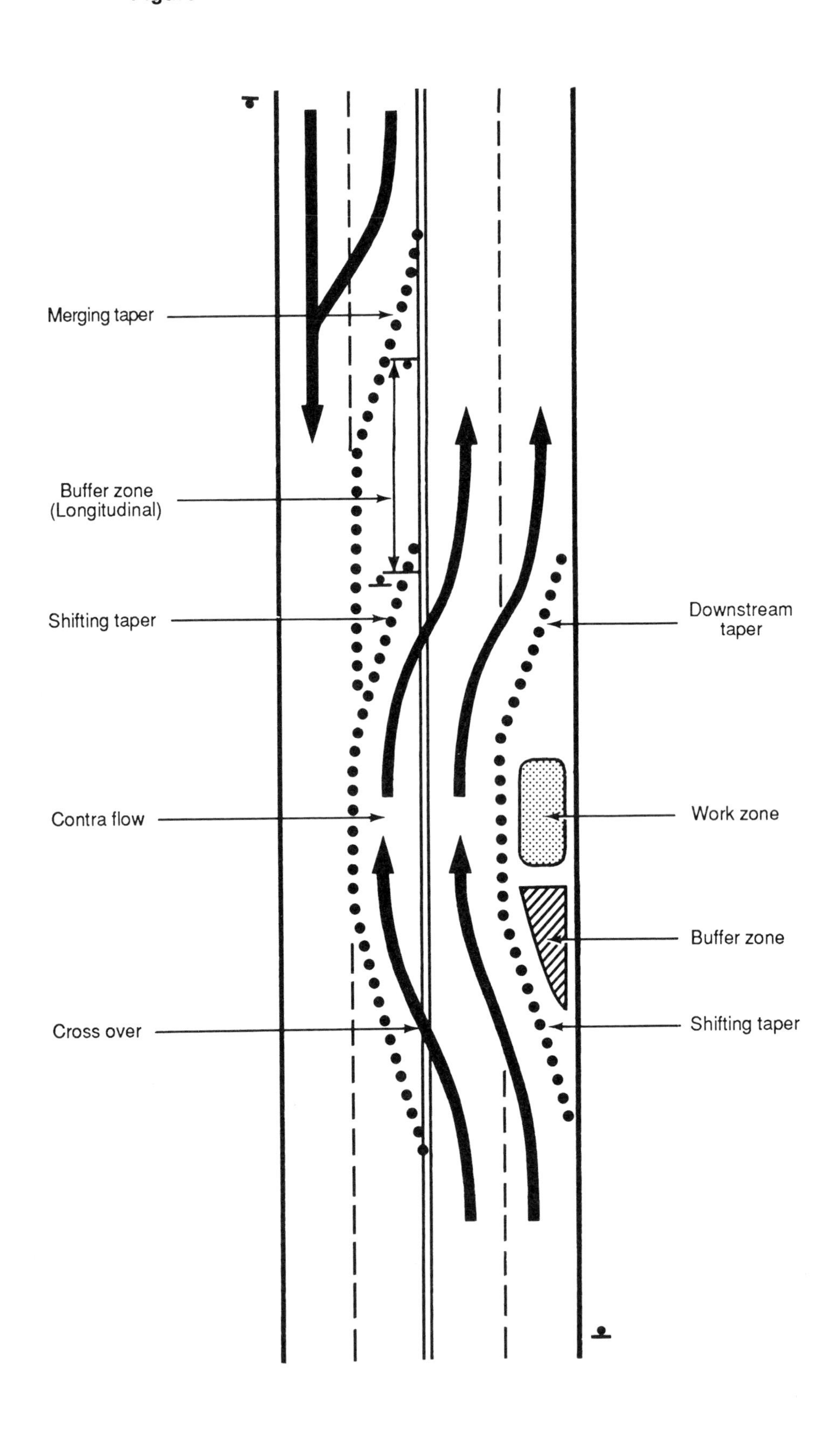

To overcome certain shortcomings, a mobile lane closure technique can be used (see Section V.8.), for instance for some routine maintenance tasks -- such as road markings -- which require frequent successive lane closures. These may often obstruct only a few metres of lane, while the rest of it -- which may be barred from normal traffic for several kilometers -- shows little evidence of activity to passing motorists. In addition, time and expense are incurred in setting out and removing a fixed closure, which any how should not exceed 2 km. Work zones along a route with mobile lane closures should be grouped so as to run in sequence wherever possible, in order to reduce "dead mileage" between them. It is also possible to operate the mobile lane closure successfully through junctions. If traffic flow is light and distance between zones is short (2 to 3 km) the lane closure technique works well by moving at moderate speed (25 km/h), the vehicle platoon formed remains intact from one work zone to the next.

V.2.2. Methods

Traffic using lanes which are to be closed should have time and space for merging with traffic in the next parallel lane as well as transfer to provisional or altered lanes, or both. Normally this requires some reduction in speed, but it should be kept to a minimum if successful merging is to be achieved.

The critical information for approaching drivers is which lane is blocked, so that they can begin moving into the open lane(s) at an early stage, before being trapped behind a platoon and being obliged to switch to the open lane with a much slower platoon speed.

Wherever possible -- normally in stationary work zones -- it is preferable to close first the fastest lane and not the slowest, even if the work zone occupies the latter. The reason for this is that slow commercial vehicles are more reluctant to give way than the more manoeuvrable cars which use the fast lane; reduction in speed is also more easily achieved. If the work zone occupies a centre lane of a multilane highway, it is recommended to also close the adjacent lane to avoid an "island" situation.

Taper for stationary lane closures should be straight, with a length (m) of not less than:

- -- 0.6V to V in rural divided highways, or rural single carriageways (e.g. a length of 60m to 100m for 100Km/h) with posted speed of 100 km/h or more, and
- -- $(V/12.5)^2$ to V in all other circumstances,

where V is the approach speed in km/h.

If two or more lanes are to be closed, a common but not universal practice is to do it one at a time, starting with the fastest lane; and between two consecutive tapers a constant width section should be left, of a minimum length (m) of not less than 0.85 to 1.25 V : this length can be used for speed reduction if advisable.

The maximum length of a lane closure depends on the traffic volume and the number of remaining lanes. Normally it should not exceed 3 km, but on some motorways lane closures up to 9 km in length have operated satisfactorily with ADT's of 14 000.

Where overhead gantries, either permanent or temporarily erected, are available, use of variable message signs greatly facilitates lane closure.

V.3. DIVERSIONS (TOTAL OR PARTIAL)

V.3.1. Detours

Total (or at least partial) diversion of traffic to another facility (generally a road of lesser category) could at first be regarded as the safest policy for the work zone. However, it is seldom acceptable except with low traffic volumes: in most cases it represents an intolerable nuisance for users, especially in urban areas where the surrounding network is already saturated, or with high traffic volumes which cannot be easily accomodated by smaller roads. Some negative aspects of detours are:

-- Longer driving time;
-- More delays and higher operating costs;
-- Lower service level;
-- Higher accident rates than at the work zone itself;
-- Deterioration and/or congestion of alternative route;
-- User confusion, especially with partial diversion.

In any case, traffic detours require:

-- That the alternative route be compatible with the additional traffic;

-- That driver information be very efficient;

-- That the alternative route be marked throughout in a very clear way, especially for partial diversion, even by variable message signs regulated according to traffic volume on either route.

There is no special evidence that the sole presence of work zones makes drivers spontaneously use alternative routes, except if they are clearly advertised and identified throughout. For low to moderate traffic and work zones of short duration and length it is sometimes possible to construct a temporary diversion, which has to be maintained in good operating condition. More permanent diversions should be used only for works of long duration, in order to maintain the total number of available lanes when no other policies are possible.

V.3.2. Contra-flow (2, 3)

A possible traffic diversion management scheme, suited to situations when the work zone occupies one carriageway of a major dual road (especially in urban or suburban areas where interchanges are close together) is 2-way traffic operation on the remaining carriageway by means of a contra-flow system. This is done by crossing the median through a suitable opening -- crossover -- either existing or temporary (4).

It can be "partial" or "full"; in the first case, only part of the traffic is diverted to the intact carriageway, while other vehicles continue to use the affected carriageway. Full contra-flow means that all traffic is diverted to the intact carriageway, and is often associated with narrower lanes and/or use of a hard shoulder. Partial contra-flow is usually segregated (only passenger cars in the contra-flow lane); full contra-flow is usually unsegregated.

Crossovers should be placed far enough from the activity area to protect it from errant vehicles, and should be designed for expected operating speeds -- no less than 15 km/h below the 85 percentile speed -- (see Sub-Section V.6.2.). Flat medians are preferable to superelevated ones. Reasonable shoulder widths and clear roadside areas should be provided.

The length of contra-flow lanes is normally related to the distance between available median crossings (unless they are built specially for this purpose), and should normally not exceed 6 km for heavy traffic (9 km if segregated); with low traffic volumes lengths of up to 24 km have been reached. Duration of the work, ease of setting up and removing necessary traffic control devices, and past accident records are also relevant.

Separation from the opposing lane(s) in the same carriageway should be emphasized by provisional markings and flexible beacons; where space allows, it is recommended to duplicate such devices, thus creating a buffer zone from about 0.5 m (minimum) to 1 m (desirable) or even one lane wide (possibly to be opened at traffic peaks). Circumstances warranting, a temporary longitudinal barrier can be erected in the crossover, more seldom in the buffer zone (where the barrier prevents wrong manoeuvres at exit ramps).

Since contra-flow single lanes have small or no shoulders, traffic flow can be impaired or even break down due to an incident, accident or other cause. Refuges can be provided in the median to accomodate vehicle breakdowns, and a fast intervention system -- with light and heavy recovery vehicles situated at each end of the work zone, available on a 24 hours standby -- should be set up (5).

Incident detection can be achieved by using several methods and/or combining some of them:

-- Regular patrols through the work zone;

-- Visual checks from a centrally situated vantage point (perhaps a specially constructed lookout tower);

-- Closed circuit television (portable all-weather cameras mounted on lighting columns or poles at intervals through the work zone, providing comprehensive coverage over 500 m sections).

Information from all these sources should be relayed to a central control point, with telephone and/or radio links to the recovery vehicles and emergency services, to ensure quick response to any incident (15 minutes being considered as the maximum intervention time).

V.4. SPEED CONTROL (6)

The traffic management techniques described in this Chapter, such as lane closure or lane changes, often effect traffic speeds changing them from their normal operating level, and can give rise to queuing. In addition there is an associated increased risk of collision between vehicles, equipment and work site personnel.

Speed limitation is an easy way of limiting damages and subsequent claims, but not the only one. It should be remembered that most Highway Codes give to the "work zone" sign the legal meaning of advising drivers of the possibility of having to adapt their speed to difficult driving conditions while moving through the work zone.

Speed is also related to the traffic flow passing through the facility. In fact, maximum flow is achieved when speed is around 80 to 85 km/h, with about 10 per cent reduction on free-flow values. Even with great reductions in speed, it has been found that the ensuing delay is seldom the main concern for motorists, who care more about overtaking restrictions, queue-forming, and rear-end collisions.

Approach speeds, especially with low traffic volumes, often exceed limits set by law or by the signs posted; it is therefore advisable to make realistic estimates, of the 85th percentile speed performing measurements, if need be.

The kinetic energy of the vehicle determines both the stopping distance and the deceleration upon impact in case of collision, is the main parameter when fixing speed limit levels. In the case of potential damage to unprotected workstaff or equipment in the work zone, or of hitting obstacles such as a trench or falsework, a larger reduction in speed is needed than in situations where adequate protective barriers are installed.

To be observed (and enforced), speed limits should appear reasonable; they should be set as high as possible, considering the distance to possible impact locations, potential damage, and the presence of barriers.

Frequently because of routine, carelessness or fear of responsibility, speed is unnecessarily reduced or, worse still, unrealistic and hard-to-justify limits are set which debase the credibility of the traffic management measures.

Low speed limits should not be prolonged through long stretches; normal speed should be resumed as soon as possible.

On high speed divided highways, such as motorways, speed should not be reduced below:

-- Usual (work-free) limits in case of small road space encroachments;
-- 100 km/h for shoulder work, 3-to-2 lane reduction, standard width lanes, or work zone protected by barriers;
-- 80 km/h for 2-to-1 lane reduction or narrow lanes;
-- 70 km/h for reversible lanes;
-- 60 km/h for lane alteration (specially median crossovers);
-- 50 km/h for median crossovers of limited geometrics.

On other types of highways speed should not be reduced below 50 km/h (40 for shuttle operation). No limit should be imposed, if work is off the carriageway.

To reduce speed, the most frequently used policy is a set of suitable vertical signs, the effect of which is greatly enhanced by the obvious presence of police officers and/or stationary police cars. The first sign should be visible from such a distance as to enable drivers to drive past it -- after a 2 sec reaction time -- at the posted speed with a deceleration rate of 5 km/h/sec (desirable) or 10 km/h/sec (maximum), starting from the approach speed (see Figure V.2). Reductions of more than 30 km/h call for more than one sign, based on the same deceleration rate, each one visible from the one before. Police or flaggers may be used. If a complete stop is envisaged, the first stop line (including the receding queue) should be visible from the last sign.

There is a tendency to complement sign action through subliminal means (chicanes, reduced carriageway width). As an example, the Table V.1 relates available width to reduced speed at work zones, without reduction in capacity.

Table V.1

RELATIONSHIP BETWEEN LANE WIDTH AND SPEED

Available width (m)		Reduced speed (km/h)
1 lane	2 lanes	
3.85	7.50	100
3.70	7.25	90
3.55	7.00	80
3.40	6.75	70
3.30	6.50	60
3.20	6.25	50

Available width can be emphasized by barriers or gates. Chicanes -- with decreasing opposite radii -- should be used carefully at night, especially with high speed traffic; lighting may be necessary. Jiggle-bars, although used and effective, are considered detestable by drivers and denote poor practice, besides being prone to rear-end accidents. If speed control is an absolute must -- e.g. to avoid chipping projection in just-laid surface dressings -- pace cars can be used.

V.5. NO-OVERTAKING

Some traffic management techniques, such as lane closure, single lane operation, or shuttle, require the prohibition of overtaking manoeuvres. This is one of the factors that reduce service level more severely, especially on undivided highways. For this reason, it should be used sparingly where it is technically justified and not as an automatic companion to the "work zone" sign; and it should be waived as soon as the reasons for the prohibition disappear.

For long duration works, pavement marking is usually necessary; for shorter duration activities, signing only may be used.

Figure V. 2 SPEED REDUCTION MODEL AS RELATED TO SIGNS

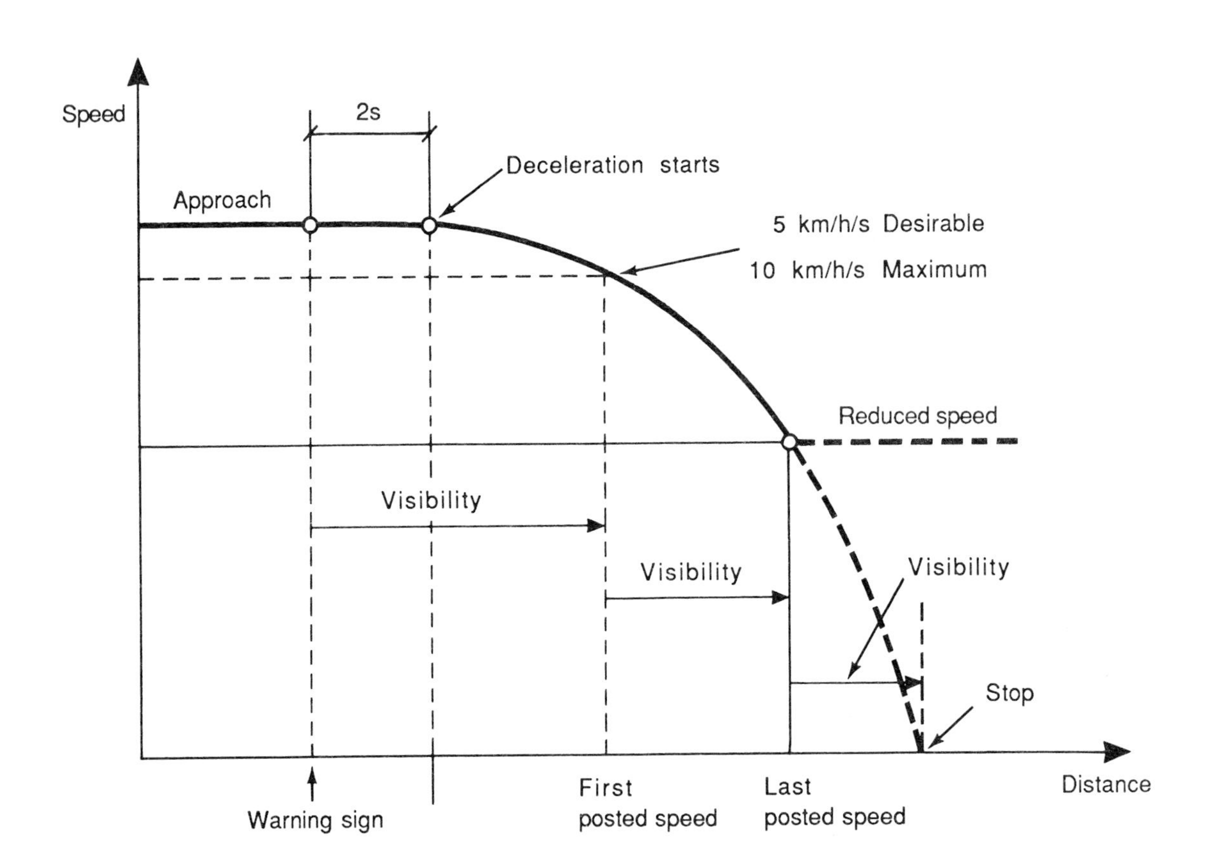

V.6. LANE ALTERATION

V.6.1. Narrow lanes

After the work zone has been delimited, the use of the remaining platform can often be maximised without a reduction in the number of lanes, by simply using narrower lanes (which at the same time control speed), by the temporary use of a hard shoulder, or both (7, 8, 9, 10).

Reduction in width should be achieved through tapers of the same dimensions as for lane closures. The minimum width of temporary lanes should be as follows:

Table V.2

MINIMUM LANE WIDTH ACCORDING TO TYPE OF FACILITY

Type of facility		Minimum lane width (m)*	
		Passenger cars only	Mixed traffic
2-way, 2-lane		2.50	2.75
Undivided; ≥ 2-lane		2.75	3.00
Divided; length of work zone	≤ 6 km	2.50	3.25
	6 to 9 km	3.00	3.25
	9 to 15 km	3.25	3.25
	≥ 15 km	3.50	3.50
Contra-flow lanes		2.75	3.00

* Add 0.25 m for U.S. conditions (wider vehicles).

Between the edge of the temporary lane and the work area itself a minimum clearance should be kept: 0.5 m minimum, 0.75 m desirable.

V.6.2. Layout alteration

Where lane layout is altered from normal to carry traffic to other parts of the carriageway, it should provide radii apportioned to the (constant) speed at which the provisional lanes are to be traversed, under the same criteria used for normal design. This means that the higher the speed, the larger the provisional lanes.

Where layout alteration follows lane closure, they should be separated by a normal layout section of length not less than 1.25 V(m); V being the (constant) running speed in that section, in km/h.

V.6.3. Added lanes

To maintain the total number of lanes, it is often possible to use the hard shoulder or even to widen the carriageway temporarily. In both cases, adequate bearing capacity must be ensured, especially when heavy vehicle traffic is present.

V.7. ONE-WAY OPERATION

Shuttle operation (11, 12, 13) is typical of two-way, two-lane highways with low traffic volumes, in which the work activity area occupies one lane so that two-way operation cannot be maintained. Its effect -- delays -- on traffic flow must be analysed to see whether another policy permitting two-way operation, such as a temporary diversion or altered lanes could be more convenient.

Central reversible lanes can also be used on divided highways in which the activity area occupies one full carriageway, thus providing more lanes for the dominant direction and less for the other: the situation can be reversed (e.g. morning and evening on suburban motorways with heavy commuter traffic), by reversing those lanes; however, comprehensive signing and detailed fail-safe operational procedures are required.

V.7.1. Shuttle operation

Single-lane shuttle operation requires a minimum free width ranging from 2.5 m (lorry width) to 3.5 m. Above this width, drivers find it difficult to understand why two-way traffic cannot be maintained.

Traffic may need to be brought to a standstill prior to the shuttle section, with the possible requirement to prohibit overtaking on the approach. Sufficient time should be allotted to permit the shuttle lane to empty in one direction before opposing traffic is allowed to enter it.

It is important, especially with high traffic volumes, to take account of the quick upstream progression of the waiting queue which can lead to vehicles meeting the end of the queue before encountering warning and speed limitation signs.

Where this problem arises, depending on the available sight distance and the traffic intensity and speed, the warning sign must be advanced upstream and/or repeated; by day, a flagger or a shadow-vehicle should "walk the queue", and by night the presence of traffic signals should be clearly signed. Variable message signs have been used for this purpose (14).

Implementation of a single-lane shuttle can be done in three ways:

-- Fixed priority for traffic using the unaffected lane, through priority signs (sometimes also a single flagger): it can only be used when:

- Traffic volume is less than 800 vehicles/hour (two-way total);
- Work zone is less than 50 m (recommended) or 150 m (maximum) long (20 m for a single flagger);
- Work duration is less than 1 week and does not include the weekend;
- Both night and day visibility is such that work zone ends can see each other and can be seen from at least 300 m (recommended) or 100 m (minimum).

-- Agent regulated priority:

- Usually not possible when work activities continue overnight or on weekends;
- Readily adaptable to traffic volume variations; maximum traffic volume 850 vehicles/hour (two-way total);
- Needs from 2 to 4 otherwise unproductive agents;
- Should not be used at night except where properly lit;
- Visual or radio communication is essential (no shuttle baton allowed);
- Maximum length about 500 m (recommended) or 1 200 m (maximum);
- Regulation must be such as to limit maximum delay from about 7 minutes for ADT $\geq$ 1 000 to about 15 minutes for ADT $<$ 1 000;
- Official cars are sometimes used to lead vehicles through a work zone, checking the speed of the platoon and showing motorists the path to follow.

-- Traffic signals:

- Available during non-working hours without direct attention (only maintenance);
- Not adaptable to traffic volume variations unless vehicle-actuated;
- Maximum traffic volume 900 vehicles/hour (at longer zones with balanced flows) to 1 300 vehicles/hour (for 50 m zones);
- Maximum length 300 m (recommended) to 500 m (maximum);
- Bottom light should be flashing amber better than green;
- Cables are vulnerable to cutting and radio communication can be disrupted; the best unattended operation is though autonomous, synchronised microprocessors;
- Regulation must be such as to limit maximum delay from about 7 minutes for ADT $\geq$ 1 000 to about 15 minutes for ADT $<$ 1 000.

V.7.2. Reversible lanes

Reversible lanes are usually separated from adjacent, non-reversible ones with delineators and beacons. Variable message signs are needed to inform drivers of prevailing regulations.

V.8. TYPICAL MANAGEMENT TECHNIQUES

Where alternative routes -- partial or total -- are not possible or advisable, the different situations can normally be assimilated to one of these cases in Table V.3.

The techniques deemed advisable for these cases are commented in Annex D. They should be evaluated on a comprehensive system basis.

Table V.3

CLASSIFICATION OF POSSIBLE RECOMMENDED TECHNIQUES
ACCORDING TO THE TYPE OF FACILITY AND THE WORK ZONE LOCATION

Work zone location (Encroachment)		Type of highway				
		Undivided			Divided	
		2-lane	2+1-Lane	4-Lane	2x2-lane	2x3-lane
External				A		
Outer shoulder				B		
Median shoulder			-		C	
In median			-		D	
In carriageway:	0			B		
number of	1	E	F	G		H
necessary lane	> 1	I	E	J	K	L
closures	all			M		

The following points should be considered when applying one of these techniques for a specific field condition:

-- Drivers may not perceive or understand one or more of the devices used for traffic management at work zones. Therefore, some extra devices may be required to achieve the desired results, without oversigning;

-- Consideration must be given to what might happen if the motorist does not get the required information;

-- The level of protection used and the delivery of the message should be related to the level of hazard; more emphatic messages and a higher level of protection are needed for high hazard situations;

-- Where possible, a recovery space or buffer zone should be provided.

For short duration and mobile operations, use of portable and dynamic devices is desirable. Portable devices are easier to move along with the operation. Dynamic devices can be changed quickly in response to a change in traffic conditions. Amongst the devices frequently used for short-duration, mobile and moving operations traffic management are (15):

-- Arrow panels and/or variable message signs;

-- Vehicles -- shadow, barrier and advance warning -- arranged in a convoy on which some of the above devices are displayed, so that a mobile information system accompanies the work team.

Shadow and barrier vehicles (16, 17, 18, 19) must be properly positioned with respect to the work team. In general, they are equipped with crash cushions. If they are too close when hit, they may slide and endanger the work staff; if too far back, drivers may pass the barrier vehicles and go back to the lane under work, thus impairing their function.

V.9. CONCLUSIONS

Many traffic management techniques are available for longer duration operations:

-- Lane closure use must be moderate with careful preparation, particularly as regards signing;
-- Additional lanes can be opened on shoulder or the median;
-- Narrow lanes help both to maintain capacity and to reduce speed;
-- Contra-flow lanes in the case of dual carriageway facilities are in increasing use;
-- Detours on the secondary network are seldom acceptable;
-- Shuttle operation applicability is restricted by length and traffic volume criteria;
-- Speed control is often over emphasized and poorly effective.

Short duration, or mobile operations need to be adapted to varying situations by using portable or dynamic techniques with official vehicles.

On the basis of research and experience at hand, it is now possible to specify efficient standard techniques ensuring acceptable levels of safety.

V.10. RECOMMENDATIONS

The following recommendations can be put forward:

-- Capacity restrictions must be carefully evaluated and monitored;
-- Lane closure should normally start from the fast lane;
-- Buffer zones should be provided whenever possible;
-- Incident control is important, especially with contra-flow techniques;

-- Speed limits should be realistic; they should be supported by appropriate accompanying measures and not only rely on signing;
-- Research is especially needed on i) vehicle merging models; and ii) speed/lane width relationships;
-- Studies on accident rates and traffic capacity associated with the various basic strategies are required.

REFERENCES

1. DEPARTMENT OF TRANSPORT. Short duration stops on trunk roads (including motorways) for inspection purposes - traffic hazards. Departmental Advice Note TA 2/79 rev. 1. Department of Transport. Roads and Local Transport Directorate. London, 1979.

2. CETE DE L'EST. Exploitation sous chantier -- basculement partiel de circulation. SETRA, Mission sécurité Routière, Note d'Information No. 3. Ministère de l'Urbanisme, du Logement et des Transports. DR-DSCR. Bagneux, 1986.

3. SETRA/DTCS. Expoitation sous chantier - mesures d'exploitation du chantier de réfection de l'autoroute A6. SETRA, Mission Sécurité Routière, Note d'Information No. 16. Ministère de l'Equipement, du Logement, de l'Aménagement du Territoire et des Transports. DR-DSCR. Bagneux, 1986.

4. 3º COMITATO TECNICO DELL'ASSOCIAZIONE. GRUPPO DI LAVORO "VARCHI". I Varchi Nello Spartitraffico - una panoramica aggiornata. Associazione Italiana Società Concessionarie Autostrade e Trafori. Roma, 1984.

5. CETE DE L'OUEST. Exploitation sous chantier - le système d'information de la Vendée. SETRA, Mission Sécurité Routière, Note d'Information No. 5. Ministère de l'Urbanisme, du Logement et des Transports. DR-DSCR. Bagneux, 1986.

6. JARVIS, JR. The effectiveness of road work speed limit signs. Australian Road Research Board. Nunawading, September, 1983.

7. MACLEAN, AD. M6 reconstruction 1976: Two-way traffic using narrow lanes. Supplementary Report 474. Transport and Road Research Laboratory. Crowthorne, 1979.

8. MACLEAN, AD and GREENWAY, M. Crawler lane construction on M5: The use of narrow lanes. Laboratory Report 782. Transport and Road Research Laboratory. Crowthorne, 1977.

9. TRANSPORT AND ROAD RESEARCH LABORATORY. Narrow lane techniques at roadworks on dual carriageways. Leaflet LF838. Transport and Road Research Laboratory. Crowthorne, 1979.

10. TRANSPORT AND ROAD RESEARCH LABORATORY. Examples of application of narrow lane systems on motorways. Leaflet LF840. Transport and Road Research Laboratory. Crowthorne, 1979.

11. SETRA/DTCS. Exploitation sous chantier - les alternats - guide technique. Ministère de l'Equipement, du Logement, de l'Aménagement du Territoire et des Transports. DR-DSCR. Bagneux, 1986.

12 SUMMERSGILL, I. The control of shuttle working at roadworks. Laboratory Report 1024. Transport and Road Research Laboratory. Crowthorne, 1981.

13. TRANSPORT AND ROAD RESEARCH LABORATORY. Control of shuttle working on single carriageway roads. Leaflet LF797. Transport and Road Research Laboratory. Crowthorne, 1979.

14. AMERICAN TRAFFIC SAFETY SERVICES ASSOCIATION. Flagging handbook. American Traffic Safety Services Association. Fredericksburg, 1987.

15. FAULKNER, MJS and DUDEK, CL. Field evaluation of moving maintenance operations on Texas urban freeways. Transportation Research Record 864. Transportation Research Board, National Research Council, National Academy of Sciences. Washington DC, 1982.

16. DEPARTMENT OF TRANSPORT. Trunk road motorways and all-purpose dual carriageway trunk roads - mobile or short duration static lane closures using vehicle mounted signs. Departmental Advice Note TA 55/87. Department of Transport. Highways and Traffic Directorate. London, 1987.

17. DEPARTMENT OF TRANSPORT. Trunk road motorways and all-purpose dual carriageway trunk roads - mobile or short duration static lane closures using vehicle mounted signs. Departmental Standard TD 29/87. Department of Transport. Highways and Traffic Directorate. London, 1987.

18. HARLOW, WA and MATTHEWS, DH. Safety at roadworks. Traffic Engineering and Control. London, October 1987.

19. MARLOW, M and HARLOW, WA. The development of mobile lane closure techniques on motorways. Traffic Engineering and Control. London, 1987.

20. UNITED NATIONS. Economic and Social Council. Economic Commission for Europe. Inland Transport Committee and Working Party on Road Transport. Group of experts on Road Traffic Safety. Projet de recommandation sur la signalisation et la sécurité des chantiers de construction routière. Restricted. Geneva, 1985.

21. UNITED NATIONS. Economic and Social Council. Economic Commission for Europe. Inland Transport Committee and Working Party on Road Transport. Group of experts on Road Traffic Safety. Projet de recommandation sur la signalisation et la sécurité des chantiers de construction routière - révision I. Restricted. Geneva, 1986.

22. MINISTERIO DE OBRAS PUBLICAS Y URBANISMO. DIRECCION GENERAL DE CARRETERAS. Norma de Carreteras 8.3-IC. "Senalizacion de Obras". Servicio de Publicaciones, Secretaria General Técnica. Madrid, 1987.

23. SWEDISH ROAD SAFETY OFFICE (TRAFIKSAKERHETSVERKET). Handbok Utmärkning vid Vägarbeten. Borlänge, 1984 (updated 1989).

24. US DOT, FEDERAL HIGHWAY ADMINISTRATION. Manual on uniform traffic devices for streets and highways. Superintendent of Documents, US Government Printing Office. Washington DC, 1978 (updated in 1979, 1983, 1984 and 1986).

25. US DOT, FEDERAL HIGHWAY ADMINISTRATION. Work zone traffic control - standards and guidelines - reprinted from Part VI of Manual on uniform traffic devices for streets and highways. Superintendent of Documents, US Government Printing Office. Washington DC, 1985.

26. US DOT, FEDERAL HIGHWAY ADMINISTRATION. Implementation Package FHWA-IP-81-6 "Planning and scheduling work zone traffic control". Superintendent of Documents, US Government Printing Office. Washington DC, 1981.

27. US DOT, FEDERAL HIGHWAY ADMINISTRATION. Traffic safety in highway and street work zones: Summary of findings and recommendations. Superintendent of Documents, US Government Printing Office. Washington DC, 1985.

28. US DOT, FEDERAL HIGHWAY ADMINISTRATION. Traffic management during major highway reconstruction (Abbreviated case studies). National Technical Information Service. Springfield, 1987.

29. COUNTY AND CITY ENGINEERS' ASSOCIATION and AN FORAS FORBARTHA TEORANTHA. Guidelines for traffic control at rural roadworks -- draft. County and City Engineers' Association and An Foras Forbartha Teoranta. Dublin, 1986.

30. McGUINNESS, P. Traffic control at roadworks -- current legislation and practices (Confidential). An Foras Forbartha Teoranta. Dublin, 1984.

31. MINISTERE DES TRAVAUX PUBLICS. Arrêté ministériel relatif à la signalisation des chantiers et des obstacles sur la voie publique. Ministère des Travaux Publics. Brussels, 1977.

32. SETRA/CSTR. Signalisation routière -- 8ème Partie: signalisation temporaire. Ministère de l'Equipement, du Logement, de L'Aménagement du Territoire et des Transports and Ministère de l'Intérieur. Bagneux, 1987.

33. MINISTERE DE L'URBANISME, DU LOGEMENT ET DES TRANSPORTS. Signalisation temporaire -- manuel du chef de chantier -- Tome 3: Voies rapides. Ministère de l'Urbanisme, du Logement et des Transports. DR-DSCR. Paris, 1980.

34. MINISTERE DE L'URBANISME, DU LOGEMENT ET DES TRANSPORTS. Exploitation sous chantier - dossier pilote du directeur des travaux. Ministère de l'Urbanisme, du Logement et des Transports. DR-DSCR. Paris, 1978.

35. DER BUNDESMINISTER FUR VERKEHR. Richtlinien für die Sicherung von Arbeitsstellen an Strassen (RSA). Verkehrsblatt-Verlag. Dortmund, 1980, stand: 1986.

36. SCHMUCK, A. Strassenerhaltung mit System - Grundlagen des Managements. Kirschbaumverlag. Bonn, 1987.

37. MINISTERO DEI LAVORI PUBBLICI. Signaletica relativa a lavori nelle autostrade en nelle strade con analoghe caratteristiche. Circolare No. 2900. Ministero dei Lavori Pubblici. Rome, 1984.

38. ALBERUCCI, E. Organizzazione della circolazione nelle zone interessate da lavori stradali. 1987.

39. DEPARTMENT OF TRANSPORT. Traffic safety measures for road works - Chapter 8 of traffic sign manual. Her Majesty's Stationary Office. London, 1974.

40. DEPARTMENT OF TRANSPORT. Traffic signs and safety measures for minor works on minor roads. Departmental Advice Note TA 6/80. Department of Transport. Roads and Local Transport Directorate. London, 1980.

41. DEPARTMENT OF TRANSPORT. Control of traffic at roadworks on single carriageway roads. Departmental Advice Note TA 47/85. Department of Transport. Highways and Traffic Directorate. London, 1985.

42. CORDINGLEY, RC and JARVIS, JR. The effect of various traffic control treatments employed at roadwork sites. Australian Road Research Board Proceedings. Nunawading, 1982.

43. RAPP INGENIEURE and PLANER. Massnahmen zur Aufrechterhaltung des Verkehrs im Bereich von Bauarbeiten an Autobahnen und Strassen. VSS Forschungsauftrag Nr. 09/87. Basel, 1987.

44. NATIONAL SWEDISH ROAD AND TRAFFIC RESEARCH INSTITUTE (VTI). Protective devices and preliminary information on permanent road works on motorways. Effects on vehicle speed and lane changing. VTI. Linköping, 1979.

45. NATIONAL SWEDISH ROAD AND TRAFFIC RESEARCH INSTITUTE (VTI). Evaluation of a new method for lane reduction at road works on motorways. VTI. Linköping, 1982.

Chapter VI

TRAFFIC AND SAFETY EQUIPMENT

VI.1. SIGNS AND CHANNELISING DEVICES

VI.1.1. General provisions for traffic control devices

The purpose of traffic control devices is to help ensure the safety and efficient movement of all traffic throughout the road transport system.

The need for traffic control devices is especially acute during work zone activities. Abnormal conditions are the rule. Therefore, traffic is particularly dependent on the design, placement, and uniformity of traffic control devices for guidance and warning through and around work zones.

The basic guidelines and standards which govern the design and usage of traffic control devices should be established by each road administration (1-7).

The primary traffic control devices used most often in work zones are signs, channelising devices, and pavement markings. All devices should be retroreflective to ensure adequate conspicuity both day and night. Because of the rough handling, work zone traffic control devices should be durable and of high quality.

The design of the devices and work zone layouts are generally the responsibility of the road administration. The installation and maintenance of the devices may be the responsibility of the road authority, contractor, or police. Whoever is responsible must assume total responsibility.

When selecting traffic control devices and barriers, maintenance characteristics and ease of installation and removal must be considered to reduce worker and motorist exposure and cost as well as providing proper guidance warning. Because traffic control devices can cause serious damage and/or injury when hit, they must be crashworthy.

Signs advise, warn, and instruct the motorist on how to drive through the work zone. Channelising devices guide the motorist through the site, indicate hazardous areas, and exclude traffic from the actual work area.

Many schemes using two basic colours are currently employed: for example, red/yellow, yellow/black, red/white or blue/white in Europe and orange/white and orange/black in the United States.

VI.1.2. Signs

Traffic signs must convey their message to the motorist clearly, both day and night and in all weather conditions.

There are three major categories of signs: regulatory, warning and directional. Their design, and their application for work zone operations are described in the national standards and manuals of the individual countries (1-7).

Design Considerations

Many signs normally used elsewhere will also be applicable in work zones. Design considerations for work zone signing are:

-- Target value is a sign's inherent ability to attract a motorist's attention: it is enhanced by using larger size and better contrast with the background, thus increasing the distance at which it is detected and recognised and providing the driver with more time to react and take action.

-- Priority value is achieved when a sign is observed before any other thing and by avoiding "unnecessary" signs in the surroundings.

-- Legibility is a function of sign size, symbol sign, letter size and contrast. Adequate cleaning and maintenance are important.

-- Retroreflectivity -- all signs shall either be retroreflectorised or directly illuminated to show the same shape and colour for both day and night.

Positioning of Signs

Signs should be positioned using the following principles:

-- Locate signs where they are easily seen;

-- Place signs so drivers have time to respond;

-- As a general rule, place signs on both sides of the roadway;

-- Cover or remove signs when work is not in progress.

Sign Supports

Sign supports should yield or breakaway upon impact (20).

Signs may either be mounted on fixed roadside supports, overhead gantries, or trailer-mounted. Signs mounted on portable low-level supports are suitable for temporary conditions such as short-duration operations (one work shift or less) or changing activities.

Trailer-mounted devices such as signs, mobile advance warning boards, road-blocking boards, arrow panels, and special lighting units are often used in work zones. They should be crashworthy and a good design should be lightweight with the centre of gravity of the unit, such as a self-contained power source, as near or below the centreline of impacting vehicles.

When impacted, detached elements, fragments or other debris from the device should not penetrate or show potential for penetrating the passenger compartment or present undue hazard to the public. Any sign support ballast should be granular material in a container that will split on impact. Large pieces of concrete or rocks should not be used as ballast.

Straw bales can be used as supports only if they are enclosed in plastic sheeting with (red and white) stripes.

Gantries are beneficial:

-- When side-mounted signs would be obscured or difficult to mount;

-- When the demands on the driver's concentration are such that it is unreasonable and possibly dangerous to divert attention away from the traffic;

Gantries are installed:

-- At the beginning of a work zone;

-- Where traffic is to be split into traffic lanes for different destinations or routes;

-- On wide carriageways, such as, three or more lanes.

Design Standards

International symbol sign legends should be used, especially on routes with a large number of foreign drivers.

In Europe, regulatory signs are a red circle (typically 600-750 mm to as small as 100 mm in diameter) with a diagonal slash to indicate a prohibited manoeuvre, or a circle around a figure to show a restricted movement. In the United States, these signs are rectangular (600 x 760 mm) with a black legend on a white background.

Warning signs are typically of two shapes:

-- Red and white or red and yellow triangular signs with symbol legends (900-1 100 mm per side) are being used in Europe. The United States and Ireland, however, use orange and black diamond-shaped warning signs (1 220 mm per side);

-- Yellow and black rectangular advanced warning signs indicate divergence to another roadway or closure of traffic lanes (1 250 x 2 000 mm) in Europe. The United States uses orange and black rectangular signs (750 x 600 mm).

Warning signs should be placed far enough in advance to give the driver adequate time to both understand the warning and to make the required response: from 1/2 km to 4 km on rural carriageways and from 100 to 500 m on urban streets; more if queueing is expected.

The typical spacing distance between signs is 100 to 1 000 m depending on speed and volume.

Directional signs show destinations, directions, distances, services, points of interest, and other geographical or cultural information. They may be used where their placement does not distract from the more important regulatory and warning signs. They are required in work zones as follows. (See Figure VI.1.):

-- Standard route signing to the extent that temporary route changes are necessary;

-- Directional and route number signs when used with diversionary routing;

-- Special information signs relating to the work being done such as: DIVERGENCE SIGNING, ROAD WORK NEXT X KM, END OF ROAD WORKS, etc.

On diversionary routes, route signs and confirmation markers should be periodically repeated.

Courtesy (public information) signs advise the motorists of special situations caused by the work activities. Typical messages are:

-- Road Work: 1st June -- 30th July;

-- Expect Delays; Sorry For The Delay;

-- Take Alternate Routes;

-- Two Way Traffic -- Next X km.

The motorists are more tolerant of inconveniences and delays if they are informed in advance.

Mobile warning boards should be used only on separated roadways. Also a road-blocking board should be used if a lane will be closed. The warning board should be placed on the right shoulder at about 600 to 1 000 metres before the road-blocking board.

The warning board should be equipped with two flashing lights, preferably halogen lights and an automatic dimmer to adjust for changed lighting conditions (see Figure VI.2.).

The road-blocking board is equipped with a light warning device (two short flashing lights and a lighted arrow) emitting amber light (see Figure VI.3.).

Road-blocking barriers or lane closure boards serve as a visual and physical barrier and reinforce the need to change direction. They are used at right angles to the line of traffic. The typical length is 1.25 to 3.00 m and between 150 and 200 mm in depth.

They are vertically hatched in red and white colours. Sign display trailers and road-blocking boards are a simple and effective aid for

Figure VI.1 EXAMPLES OF DIFFERENT DIRECTIONAL SIGNS

Change to opposite carriageway with one lane width specified

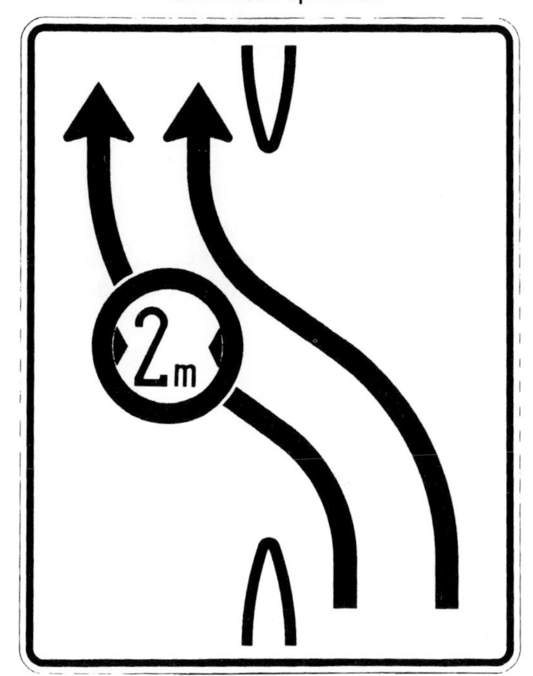

Schematic diagram

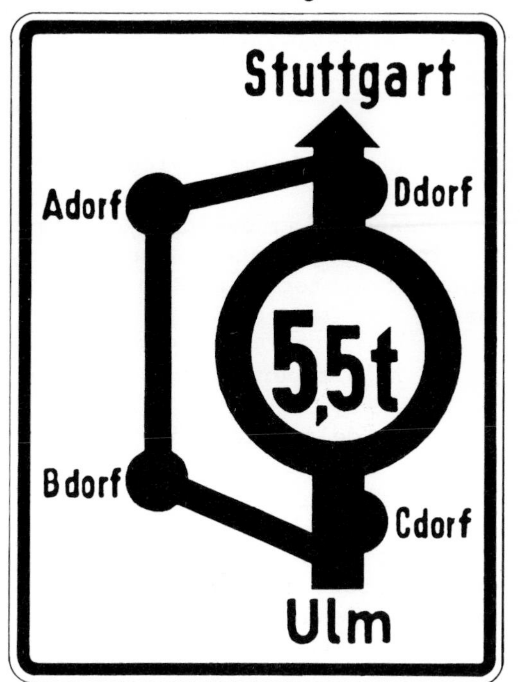

Reduction of number of lanes

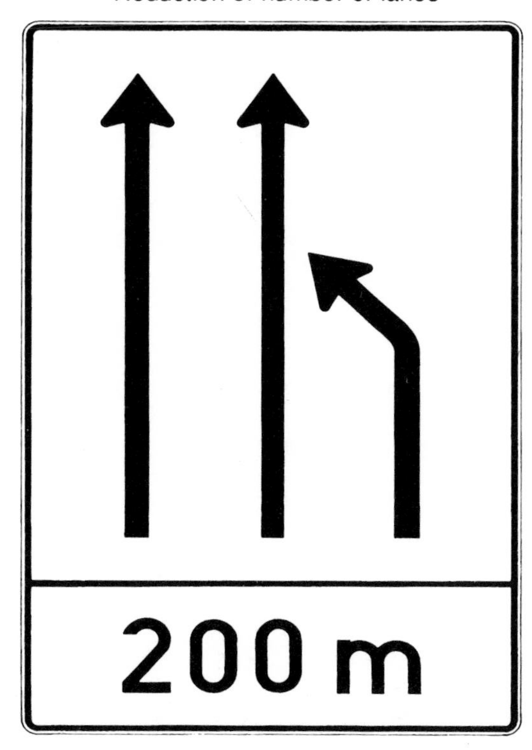

channelising traffic, especially when they are equipped with an extra large traffic sign and flashing beacons.

Chevron signs indicate the direction of a deviation and to guard the obstruction which is the cause of the change of direction. The typical dimensions are 200-800 mm in depth and 900 mm for the minimum length with no maximum. These signs may be used as a series of separate minimum lengths or in one continuous length. They should not be used as a continuous fence or barrier parallel to a relatively straight carriageway.

VI.1.3. Channelising devices

Channelising devices are cones, traffic cylinders, drums, or barriers placed in or adjacent to the roadway to control the flow of traffic. They are elements of a total system of traffic control and they have two distinct purposes:

-- As a taper to move traffic from one lane to another;

-- To delineate and guide the driver to and along a safe path.

Cones and Traffic Cylinders

Cones (0.5 to 1.0 m high and 0.3 to 0.4 m in diameter) or traffic cylinders (about 500 mm high) have normally retroreflectorised red and white bands in Europe and orange and white in the United States.

Large cones are used on high-speed roadways and on all facilities during hours of darkness or whenever more conspicuous guidance is needed.

Cones and cylinders are easily blown over or displaced unless their bases are ballasted or anchored. In some situations, it may be necessary to double the cones, use heavier weighted cones, use special weighted bases, or use weights such as sand bag rings to provide increased stability but this weight should not present a hazard.

In general, cones have greater target value than cylinders. In the United States they may be enhanced in daytime by insertion of a flag in the top. Their advantages are as follows:

-- Minor impediments to traffic flow and capacity;

-- Well recognised and understood, without damaging vehicle when hit;

-- Easily stored and transported;

In addition, traffic cylinders can be fastened to the pavement, and self-restoring when hit.

Their disadvantages are as follows:

-- Minimal respect by drivers;

-- Easily penetrated, displaced and knocked over; and

Figure VI. 2 MOBILE WARNING BOARD

Figure VI. 3 ROAD BLOCKING BOARD EQUIPPED WITH A LIGHT WARNING DEVICE

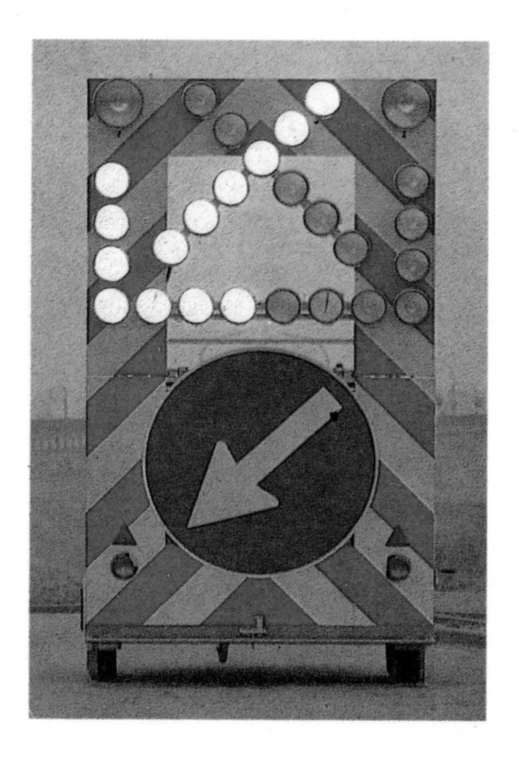

-- Special treatment for night-time;

Cones or cylinders should be checked and reset periodically.

Recently developed self-dissolving foam cones are being used to protect pavement marking paint. They are automatically ejected on the markings at predetermined intervals and start dissolving within 30 minutes.

Marker Posts

Marker posts (0.2 m to 0.3 m in width and 0.6 to 1.0 m in height) have retroreflective striping sloped down toward the side of which traffic is to pass. They are mounted on a single lightweight post driven into the ground or ballasted with the bottom at least 0.2 m above the roadway. At night, beacons may be placed on the posts as needed.

These posts are effective as traffic separators or for channelisation on narrow shoulders where available lateral spacing is limited.

Drums

Drums (about 1 m high and 0.3 m in diameter) with retroreflective bands are made of plastic or steel.

Plastic drums are lighter, pose less hazard to vehicles and workers, can be nested for easy transportation and storage, and generally have one or more flat sides to preclude rolling.

Drums are used as either channelising or warning devices. They are highly visible, give the appearance of being formidable objects and, therefore, command the respect of drivers. A sandbag may be placed in the bottom of the drum. If freezing conditions may occur, drain holes should be made in the bottom.

VI.1.4. Contra-flow separation devices

Contra-flow operations on one roadway of a normally divided highway is a typical application that requires special consideration in the planning, design, and construction phases, as severe operational problems (serious head-on collisions) can arise. Chapter V discusses criteria that must be considered and the foregoing three sub-sections and Section VI.3. review the equipment useful for contra-flow separation.

VI.2. MARKINGS AND LIGHTING DEVICES

VI.2.1. Pavement markings

At work zones, temporary changes in travel paths are often necessary (lane closed, or narrowed; detours). Delineation can be done with temporary pavement markings. Markings are especially important during darkness. They often need to be changed for the various phases encountered, and the existing markings must be obliterated.

Many countries use a different coloured pavement marking, such as orange, for work zones.

Materials

Temporary markings are made of paint with retroreflective beads, thermoplastic studs (raised pavement markers), or foil (preformed adhesive-backed retroreflectorised tape). They should be placed before the traffic is changed. When this is not feasible, temporary delineation may be accomplished with lines of traffic cones, other channelising devices, strips of foil or studs.

Temporary markings should be removed immediately when no longer appropriate to avoid any conflicting marking. Use of studs or foil may be economical since they are usually easier to remove (19).

Removal of Markings

Pavement marking paint removal (8, 9) is an art and may require a combination of methods depending on the types of paint used, the number of paint coats remaining, and other road conditions. Difficulties have been compounded by improved paint durability and adhesion. Methods of removal include grinding, burning, chemical treatment, sandblasting, hydroblasting, and shot blasting.

Over-painting inappropriate markings with black paint and bituminous solution should not be used because the original lines eventually reappear as the overlying material wears away under traffic. In addition, lines covered in this way are still visible under certain conditions (i.e. low angles of illumination). However, overbanding of markings with gray or black tape has proven satisfactory.

A prime prerequisite for stripe removal is to have a minimum effect on the road surface. All of the above-listed methods will damage a pavement surface texture to some degree. The art of removal is in selecting the methods that will do the least amount of damage and do the removal properly.

Sandblasting is particularly effective when the surface is rough and porous. This method will do little damage to the bituminous surfacing and the resulting scar will be barely noticeable. Sand deposited on the pavement should be removed as the work progresses to prevent accumulations which might interfere with drainage or constitute a traffic hazard.

Hydroblasting has also been used successfully under some conditions, but ponding water could be a hazard.

Shot blasting is also effective in removing markings with minimal damage to the pavement. This system consists of metal shot being directed at high speeds at the markings. The system is self-contained, recycling the shot.

A chemical stripper is equally effective on bituminous and concrete pavement. The stripper is applied to the marking for a period determined by prior testing, and the markings are then washed off by water jets.

Also a new water-based paint is available which is resistent to weather, acids, and oils but it can be washed off with a special remover.

Studs are to be easily and quickly removed with a hand shovel or front-end loader. Foil can be easily removed by burning, grinding, or being pulled up.

VI.2.2. Lighting devices

Selective use of lighting devices may be used to supplement signs, barriers, and channelising devices. The more powerful ones, such as the arrow panel and high intensity lights, are powerful attention-getting devices during the day.

Warning Beacons

Warning beacons or lights are used to indicate hazards and to delineate the safe path of travel. They are portable, lens-directed enclosed lights. Three types of warning beacons are used:

- Low intensity flashing beacons, generally mounted on signs or barriers, are effective only at night to draw attention to warning devices on hazards in or near the roadway;

- Steady-burning low-wattage beacons used at night for delineation are commonly mounted on barriers or marker posts, to channelise the proper travel path;

- High-intensity beacons are effective both day and night on advanced warning boards, signs, and road-blocking boards.

Variable Message Signs (VMS)

Variable Message Signs (10, 11) are trailer or gantry mounted signs capable of displaying real-time information on closed lanes, routing, or speed advisories. Type of VMS include bulb or disk or rotating drum matrix. The most popular VMS is the bulb matrix which can display a steady or flashing or scrolling message.

Many of the VMS signs have a wide variety of words that can be used together to form numerous messages. A menu of predeveloped messages should be used after understanding by drivers has been tested.

VMS is cost-efficient in short duration closures characterised by decreased driver expectancy, minimum traffic volumes of 900 vehicles per hour, and limited sight distances to the closure.

Some of the guidelines for VMS suggested by the NCHRP research (10) are to be located one kilometre in advance of lane closures to supplement standard traffic control devices, but not to be considered as an alternative to arrow panels.

VMS are sometimes incorrectly used by leaving the sign with the same message for an extended period of time. The primary purpose of VMS in work zones is to advise drivers of unexpected traffic and routing situations. Prolonged use of a VMS at one location and for one purpose may reduce the sign's effectiveness.

Typical work zone applications of the VMS are: change or new diversion, lane drop, special speed control measures, and restricted sight distance where congestion occurs.

VMS can be placed on either the right or left side of a divided highway; however, when operating simultaneously on both sides they could be distracting and confusing to drivers.

Like arrow panels, VMS that use lights should be dimmed at night. Light bulbs should be replaced when more than 10 per cent are burned out.

A particular problem concerns use of too long messages: some drivers could slow or even stop to read the entire message. A driver needs at least one second per short word (up to eight characters not counting prepositions), or two seconds per unit of information (typically two words) to read and recall a well-designed message. If drivers start viewing a VMS from 1/2 kilometre at 90 km/h, they would have about four seconds to read a message, which implies that the message should be no longer than four words. VMS have limited use on routes with foreign-speaking motorists as the text is in words rather than pictorial graphics.

Nose-to-tail collisions can occur when queuing goes upstream from a work zone and extends beyond the routine advance warning signs. Motorists may be warned by queue warning VMS activated manually by remote control or by detectors. Several messages may be displayed on the sign (see Figure VI.4.).

VI.3. TEMPORARY SAFETY BARRIERS

Barriers are intended to provide containment without significant deflection or deformation under impact and to redirect errant vehicles along the barrier. Work zone safety barriers are designed to be easily relocated. They have four specific functions: i) to protect traffic from entering work areas, such as excavations or material storage sites; ii) to provide positive protection for workers; iii) to separate two-way traffic; and iv) to protect construction such as falsework for bridges and other exposed objects.

VI.3.1. Temporary longitudinal safety barriers

They include portable concrete or steel safety shape barriers and transposable separators. Their use should be based on an engineering analysis and assessment of the different factors that affect barrier need within work zones. Though no consensus on specific warrants exist, barriers are usually justified for bridge widening, roadside structures, and roadway widening.

Portable Concrete Barriers

Temporary longitudinal safety barriers are widely used in work zones to protect motorists as well as workers. However, improper use of these barriers can provide a "false sense of security" for both the motorist and the worker. Therefore, care must be taken in their design, installation, and maintenance.

Figure VI. 4 MOBILE WARNING VMS

Temporary barriers are free-standing precast concrete sections (3 to 8 metres in length) with built-in connecting devices. Barrier weight varies from 680 to 900 kg/m depending on exact cross section geometry, material and amount of reinforcement. The weight of individual segments can vary from 2 000 to 7 300 kg. These weights, even though varying by a factor of four, all require heavy equipment for movement. Adequate longitudinal reinforcement and positive connections ensure that the individual sections act as a smooth continuous unit.

Corners of barriers may be bevelled to minimise snagging of snow-ploughs and to allow placement of the barrier sections in curves.

When impacted, the mass of the barrier and friction between it and the underlying surface tend to limit movement and overturning. Each section must be properly connected to the adjacent section to provide barrier continuity to resist movement. The barrier may need to be anchored to the underlying surface to prevent lateral movement. This can be done with drift pins or anchor bolts attached to the pavement or bridge deck. The pins or bolts should not protrude beyond the face of the barrier. Another method to limit sliding is to place the barrier on a grout bed or styrofoam pad. This provides a mechanical interlock between the barrier and the pavement surface.

To perform properly and redirect vehicles, the barrier system must be capable of withstanding severe impacts. The weakest point is its connector which includes the physical connection and mating faces of adjoining barriers. The methods for connecting barrier segments vary widely.

-- All sections are to be positively connected to adjacent sections such as with a pin and loop connection (see Figure VI.5).

-- The end section must be anchored to prevent overturning and excessive sliding and shielded such as by a crash cushion.

-- Adequate clearance, at least 1 m, should be provided between the barrier and the activity area to allow for sliding of the barrier. If adequate clearance is not available, the barrier should be anchored.

-- Precautions must be taken to prevent the barrier from falling into an excavation. When placing a PCB around an excavation, the capability of the soil to withstand the pressure created by the PCB and any other objects near the cut face must be determined.

-- A PCB should only be installed if it reduces the severity of potential accidents.

Applications

The minimum length of a portable barrier system should be 30 m. It should not be placed more than 2 to 3 m from the edge of the roadway to reduce the potential of high-angle (more than 15 degrees) impacts.

Barriers may be used to channelise traffic but should not be used as the primary tapering device. Lane tapers should have more forgiving channelising devices such as cones or drums. Once the lane is closed, the barrier may be introduced. Barriers perform best when placed parallel to traffic flow.

For better night visibility, retroreflective devices or steady-burn warning beacons may be mounted along the barrier. Also, a solid edgeline may be placed on the pavement adjacent to the barrier to increase conspicuity.

Transposable Separators

Another system (12) consists of long (around 1.10 m) concrete or steel components provided with twin eyelets which enable them to be interlinked along a vertical axis. The base width is around 600 mm. They offer excellent shock resistence due to their weight and to their mode of assembly.

The elements are placed on the edge of the roadway and then positioned by a specially designed self-propelled vehicle.

Glare Screens (16, 17)

Glare screens on barriers may be used in work zones to reduce headlight glare from opposing vehicles or to block the driver's view of work zone activities which may distract from the driving tasks. Crossovers, tangents, restricted lanes, and tapers adjacent to activity areas may warrant their use. The addition of appropriate reflectorisation at intervals along the screening device enhances nighttime visual guidance.

Use of glare screens in work zones depends on many factors such as accident experience, high nighttime traffic volumes, complaints from the public, and highway geometry. Additional factors include distance between opposing traffic, lane restriction, delineation washout and worker proximity.

Figure VI. 5

PORTABLE CONCRETE BARRIERS AND CONNECTION TO ADJACENT SECTIONS

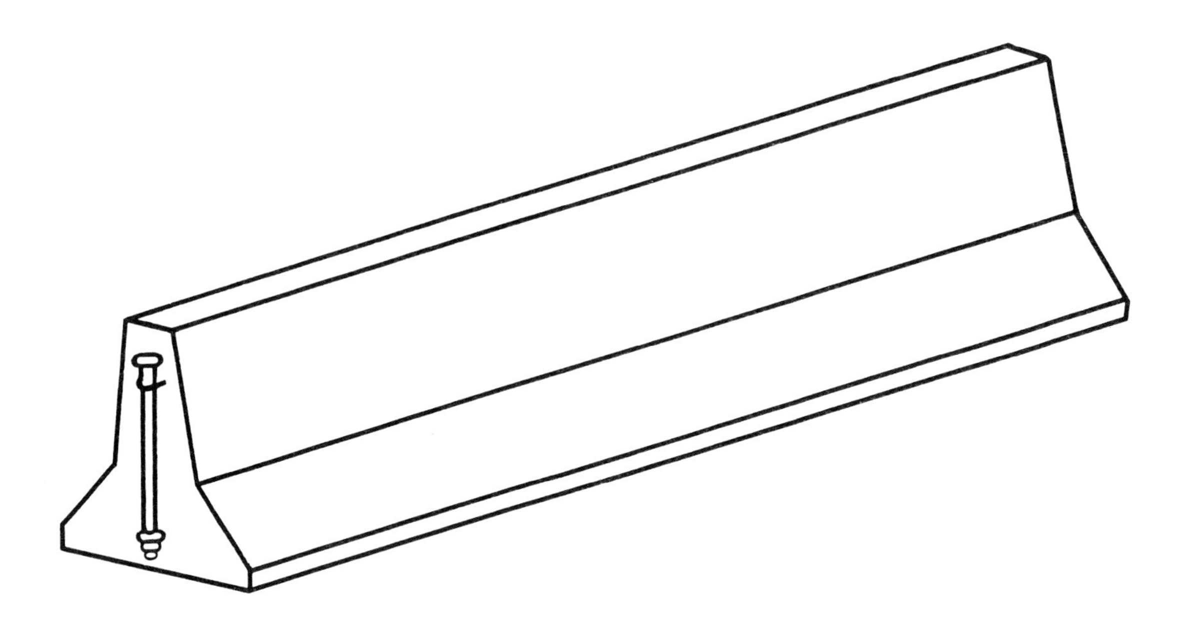

Desirable characteristics of a work zone glare screen include:

-- Effectiveness in reducing nighttime glare from opposing vehicles;

-- Prevention of total or partial dislodgement;

-- When hit, device should not penetrate the passenger compartment or present an undue hazard to workers and other traffic;

-- Portability, quick repair, and easy installation;

-- Units should correspond to and shall not extend beyond or alter the design of the barrier;

-- Surveillance and access to the opposing lane by police and emergency personnel.

VI.3.2. Crash cushions

Principles and Designs

Crash cushions (13, 16, 20) are protection systems that prevent vehicle impact with fixed obstacles by either smoothly decelerating the vehicle to a stop after a frontal impact or by redirecting it away from the hazard under a glancing or side impact. The intended function of all types of crash cushions is to dissipate the energy of the impacting vehicle either partially during a side-on impact or fully in the case of a head-on impact. This is accomplished through the principle of mechanics: "the change in kinetic energy is equal to the work done on the system".

"Crushable" crash cushions include those systems that resist the forward motion of the vehicle through continued crushing of the material of which the crash cushion is composed. In general, the crushable material is not reusable after impact. This type of system requires attachment to the obstacle being protected (or an auxiliary reaction back-up system).

"Inertia" systems do not require a back-up restraint system. They include those systems that dissipate energy through successive impacts with closely spaced individual packages of weighty material (sand, water), each impact slowing the vehicle as it moves the material.

Crash Cushion Performance

Crash cushions should exhibit some desirable characteristics:

-- Smoothly stop a vehicle within the acceptable deceleration limits to vehicle occupants when impacted in a head-on collision;

-- Redirect a vehicle safely after a side-on acute-angle impact situation (if this capability is required);

-- Remain intact after impact if it is a "crushable" type, and produce minimum debris if it is a "expendable mass" type;

-- Be capable of quick repair or restoration after impact;

-- Be compatible with the geometric and expected impact envelope characteristics at the site (space available, single or bidirectional impact expectation, etc.);

-- Be reliable and dependable under all environmental situations.

Dynamic performance criteria for crash cushions with respect to acceptable impact severity is specified under two impact situations: redirection from a glancing impact, and head-on impacts. The test criteria are:

-- For redirecting the vehicle, maximum vehicle accelerations (50 m/sec ^{2} average) measured near the centre of mass should be less than the following values:

Maximum Vehicle Acceleration (g's)

Lateral	Longitudinal	Total	Remarks
3	5	6	Preferred
5	10	12	Acceptable

These rigid body accelerations apply to impact tests at 15 degrees or less

-- For head-on impacts where the vehicle is decelerated to a stop, and where lateral accelerations are minimum, the maximum average permissible vehicle deceleration is 12 g's as calculated from vehicle impact speed and passenger compartment stopping distance.

Applications

Common applications of crash cushions include roadside and median installations. Crash cushions should be considered as an alternative to barriers, particularly for protection of potential impacts with fixed "point" hazards. Obstacles such as falsework and the end of concrete barriers are examples where crash cushions can be effectively used to reduce a lethal impact to one of relatively minor consequence.

Crash cusions have been shown to be cost-effective.

VI.3.3. Truck-mounted attenuators (TMA's)

In many short duration and mobile work zones, trucks can be used as blocking vehicles to protect workers. Large trucks are effective in preventing vehicle encroachment into the work site; however, serious injury to occupants of the impacting vehicle and truck can result. Therefore, crash cushions, called truck-mounted attenuators (TMA's) (14), have been developed; they are attached to the rear of these protective vehicles to reduce the severity of rear-end crashes. TMA's may either be trailer or truck mounted (Figure VI.3.).

TMA's may be used for moving operations such as pavement marking, mowing and roadway sweeping, or maintenance activities in high-traffic volume areas.

Shadow trucks and barrier vehicles may be equipped with a TMA. Advance sign trucks should use TMA's if they encroach on the travelled way. Protective vehicles usually are equipped with arrow panels, variable message signs, or flashing amber beacons. To increase the protection for the truck drivers, the trucks often have seatbelts and headrests.

TMA's are not suitable for specialised vehicles such as motor graders, snow removal equipment and tow trucks.

VI.4. TRAFFIC SHIFTING TECHNIQUES AND EQUIPMENT

VI.4.1. Installation and removal

Preparation

The safe and efficient installation, modification, and removal of traffic control devices at work zones can be enhanced by adequate preparations (18). This is particularly important because of the hazard associated with these activities.

Figure VI. 6 TRUCK-MOUNTED ATTENUATOR

The installation and removal of traffic control devices create situations that are often far more hazardous than the operation of the completed zone. To reduce the exposure, the installation should be done as quickly as possible. To this end, several elements must be considered before the installation of the traffic control zone:

-- Advance and start time co-ordination should be done with all affected organisations and groups.

-- All traffic devices required for the installation and maintenance of the zone should be on-hand and in good condition.

-- All crew members should be trained for their tasks, with particular emphasis on safety. Rehearsals of the projects may be necessary to assure an efficient and speedy operation.

Installation

The installation sequence is realised in the direction that traffic moves; that is, moving "downstream". The first device placed is the first advance warning sign. The installation then proceeds with the transition, activity and termination areas (see Figure IV.2.).

If traffic in both directions will be affected, such as work in the central lanes, the devices can be placed in both directions at the same time, or in one direction after the other. When one direction of traffic will be directed into the opposing lane, devices for the opposing traffic should be placed first.

Flashing arrow panels are valuable to assist the workers during placement or removal of channelising devices for lane closures.

The installer of the traffic control devices should be totally responsible for ensuring proper placement and maintenance.

In the installation procedure, work vehicles should park in a safe location to unload crews and devices, such as: legally at curb; on shoulder; or on side street.

The work vehicle may serve as the advance warning device by using its flashing/rotating beacons while the first warning signs or boards are being placed. To protect the crew, the device truck should be located upstream of the crew. This can be awkward, however, if the signs are unloaded from the rear of the truck.

On high-speed roads, a "backup", "shadow", or "protection", vehicle should be used. This vehicle should first be positioned on the shoulder some 30 m or more behind the device truck when the first signs are placed. The shadow vehicle uses special beacons or a flashing arrow panel to warn traffic. When the crew needs to work on the roadway, the shadow vehicle is moved into the travelled lane. Truck-mounted attenuators are desirable for these vehicles.

As regards the placing of channelising devices, in the case of lane closure, tapers are laid out in a straight line at the shoulder. Each channelising device is then placed in sequence moving downstream. When placed by hand, the devices should be moved out from the shoulder with the worker looking toward traffic. When tapers are installed, each device is placed further into the lane being closed.

If work space does not take the entire width of the lane the channelising devices should be placed between 0.5-1.0 m back from the lane line.

Cones may be placed either by workers on foot or from a moving vehicle, equipped with a suitable platform and railing. On high-speed roadways, a shadow vehicle should protect workers.

On earth shoulders, markers are mounted on a driven post. On structures or paved areas, they may be mounted on light-weight posts.

Modification and Removal

When possible, traffic control devices should be removed in a reverse sequence that is moving "upstream".

With no shoulders, advance warning signs are removed in the downstream direction.

Where extensive modifications are required, it may be necessary to remove the entire zone and then reinstall it in the new configuration.

Barriers require special care and planning. Normally, the lane next to the barrier must be closed while the barriers are placed or moved. This operation should be scheduled to cause as little disruption as possible.

VI.4.2. Special equipment and techniques

Special equipment has been developed to facilitate and expedite the installation process. One feature often found is a rack in which signs are loaded in the reverse sequence to that needed.

Special features of traffic control vehicles may include: flashing/ rotating strobe lights or beacons, arrow panels, or VMS, sign racks or cone chutes, power lift tailgates; worker platform and protective railing, etc.

Cone dispensers have been experimented with to automatically place or remove cones quickly and safely from a moving vehicle.

Finally, it is recommended to maintain an inventory of extra traffic control devices so that damaged devices may be readily replaced.

VI.4.3. Expressway lane closures

Expressway lane closures are of two types. "Exterior" lanes are those with a shoulder along one edge. "Interior" lanes, such as the centre lane of a three-lane roadway, are bordered by lanes on both sides. As seen in Section V.2. it is not recommended to only close the inner lane ("island situation").

The protection vehicle travels along the shoulder or exterior lane if no shoulder is available. It is equipped with a warning beacon and a flashing arrow panel. The protection vehicle then stops in a blocking position at least 30 m upstream while the first warning sign is located. This operation is repeated for all warning signs -- first for one side, then the other side of the roadway.

When all signs are in place, channelisation devices are placed. The protection vehicle gradually encroaches upon the exterior lane as the workers install the taper in front of the protection vehicle. Finally, the protection vehicle is positioned in the closed lane while the work zone channelisation is placed.

VI.5. SHUTTLE OPERATION PROCEDURES AND EQUIPMENT

Where traffic on both directions must use a single lane over a short distance, provision should be made to alternate one-way traffic through the constricted section, following the indications given in Section V.7.

VI.5.1. Signing

At "give and take" or priority assignment sites, signing should warn motorists of on-coming traffic in the single lane. Typical signs are "STOP" and "YIELD TO ON-COMING TRAFFIC", and more generally static symbols with arrows giving the fixed priority.

VI.5.2. Flaggers

Flaggers are used at work sites to intermittently stop or slow traffic. They must always be clearly visible to approaching traffic from a long enough distance to permit proper driver response to the flagging instructions before the driver enters the activity area.

A flagger should wear special clothing or uniform to be more visible and to have more authority. Because of the important responsibility of controlling traffic, flaggers must be properly trained. They may either be agents or police officers.

Red flags and lights could be used to slow down traffic. The hand-signalling devices used to regulate priority are RED/GREEN long-handled paddles, where STOP could be on the red face and SLOW or GO on the green face.

Co-ordination between flaggers could be based on clear verbal or hand signals or a radio link.

Flaggers must be able to warn other workers when an out-of-control or violator vehicle driving through the flagger station or into the activity area. Air horns or whistles are sometimes used to alert the work crew.

VI.5.3. Traffic control signals

All traffic control signal equipment shall meet the applicable standards and specifications. They must be reliable, easy to install and maintain. As cable or radio links could be damaged, the preferred co-ordination is operated by synchronised internal clocks in each signal.

One-way traffic operation requires an all-red interval of sufficient duration for traffic to clear the zone at the minimum operating speed in the work area. If the signal is operated manually, both entries into the section must be clearly visible from the switching device.

VI.6. SHORT-DURATION OPERATIONS AND EQUIPMENT

Most maintenance and utility operations and some construction work are short duration, or mobile. Because of the dynamic and temporary nature of these operations, traffic controls may vary from those used for long-duration operations. Special devices and procedures should also be used.

VI.6.1. Signing

Signs for activity area operations of short duration are generally mounted on the vehicles and/or placed on the shoulder. If possible, signing should never be further than 500 m from the activity area. Because these signs must be frequently moved, a special vehicle or trailer may be used to carry the signs. Advance warning boards and road-blocking boards are effective types of signing.

The road-blocking board is often equipped with short flash lights and a luminous arrow, functioning with an adaptation to light conditions allowing for a reduction down to 50 per cent. The luminous arrow could light up with a frequency of 35 (45) light impulse/minute. The period of illumination could be twice as long as the dark period. In the middle of the dark period the flash lights could light up (Figure VI.3).

These devices could be mounted on a trailer which is drawn by a site vehicle, or be directly fixed to the vehicle.

VI.6.2. Warning beacons

Amber rotating lights and flashes are effective for gaining driver attention. They should be used on maintenance vehicles performing short-duration operations, where a full traffic control zone is impractical, on vehicles performing moving or intermittent stop operations and on shadow vehicles. Typical flashing warning lights are of 50-70 w halogen bulb with a 300 mm diameter. Each vehicle should be equipped with at least two lights.

VI.6.3. Arrow panels

These sign panels, with a matrix of lights capable of either flashing or sequential arrow displays, are intended to supplement other traffic control devices.

Arrow panels provide additional advance warning and directional information where traffic must be shifted laterally along the roadway. Arrow panels are effective in encouraging drivers to leave the closed lane sooner.

Placement of arrow panels should be varied as needed to achieve the desired recognition distance. Care must be taken in their placement near curves, ramps, median crossovers, and side-road intersections. For stationary lane closures, the preferred location for the arrow panel is on the shoulder near the start of the taper. If the shoulder is too narrow, the panel should be placed in the closed lane behind the channelising devices.

In mobile operations, the arrow panel should be placed on a separate vehicle upstream of the work vehicle, in the closed lane. It should not be used on two-lane highways because it could encourage a careless use of the lane for opposite direction traffic.

Large (1.2 x 2.4 m) arrow panels can be seen from a kilometre away, and are especially effective in high-volume or high-speed traffic.

When used at night panels should be checked to make sure they are not blinding drivers. The use of these medium-to-high intensity lights is very important. However, to provide motorists with better information on speed differentials, a flashing light (flasher or four-way flashers) is useful.

VI.6.4. Marking and clothing

Vehicle Markings

The work vehicle, especially the rear, should be properly marked with retroreflective material, beacons, or warning flags.

Safety Clothing

The use of retroreflective and fluorescent clothing such as a vest, shirt, jacket or coveralls is as much necessary for all workers as for those who are not separated from the traffic.

VI.7. CONCLUSIONS

The traffic control devices should be:

-- Simple to be understood by the motorists, whether local, tourist or foreign;

-- Readily seen and followed by the motorist, day and night or during adverse weather: target value, priority value, legibility and retroreflectivity;

-- Located sufficiently in advance to provide motorist time to react to the situation.

The traffic barriers are used to protect motorists, workers and work areas. However, since they can be hazardous to motorists, their use should be based on engineering studies and on safety specifications.

Traffic control devices and barriers:

-- Must be fabricated, installed and maintained in accordance with approved standards and procedures;

-- When selecting, ease of installation, removal and maintenance as well as cost must be considered;

-- The appropriate type and amount must be provided for each work zone;

-- When not needed, they must be removed;

-- The safety and efficiency of installing, modifying and removing can be enhanced by adequate preparation.

VI.8. RECOMMENDATIONS

The following should be developed and used:

-- Signs using pictograms rather than words;

-- Crashworthy devices easy to install, remove and relocate;

-- Temporary pavement marking easy to install and remove;

-- Additional crash cushion designs;

-- Guidelines for the use of variable message signs;

-- Uniform traffic control devices among the countries, especially in Europe.

There is a clear need for international harmonization and standardization. ECE should be asked to lay more emphasis on the whole issue of signing and marking of work sites.

REFERENCES

1. MINISTERE DE L'INTERIEUR. Signalisation routière. Livre 1. Ministère de l'Intérieur. Paris, 1987.

2. MINISTERE DE L'URBANISME. Signalisation temporaire, Manuel du chef de chantier. SETRA. Paris, 1980.

3. MINISTRY OF TRANSPORT. Traffic safety measures for road works. Traffic sign manual, Chapter 8. Ministry of Transport, HMSO. London, 1974.

4. DER BUNDESMINISTER FÜR VERKEHR. Richtlinien für die Sicherung von Arbeitsstellen au Strassen. Der Bundesminister für Verkehr. Bonn, 1986.

5. MINISTERIO DE OBRAS PUBLICAS Y URBANISMO. Senalizacion de Obras. Ministerio de Obras Publicas y Urbanismo. Madrid, 1987.

6. SWEDISH ROAD SAFETY OFFICE (Trafiksäkerhetsverhet). Handbok, Utmärkning vid Vägarbeten. Borlänge, 1984 (updated 1989).

7. US DOT, FEDERAL HIGHWAY ADMINISTRATION. Work zone traffic control -- standards and guidelines. FHWA. Washington, DC, 1985.

8. BRYDEN, JE and KENYON, WD. Methods for removal of pavement markings. Research Report 130. New York Department of Transportation. Albany, New York, 1986.

9. MINISTERE DE L'URBANISME. Les produits de marquage et leur mise en oeuvre: techniques d'effaçage. Note d'information 02. SETRA. Paris, 1985.

10. HANSCOM, FR. Effectiveness of changeable message displays in advance of high-speed freeway lane closures. NCHRP Report 235, Transportation Research Board. Washington, DC, 1981.

11. DUDEK, CL. Portable changeable message signs at work zones. Report No. FHWA/TX-85/07+292-4. Texas Department of Highways and Public Transportation. Texas, July, 1984.

12. MESQUI, J and CHAUSSOY, C. Expérimentation d'un séparateur béton transposable sur le chantier de l'autoroute A1. Direction départementale de l'Equipement de Seine-Saint-Denis. Paris, 1987

13. US DOT, FEDERAL HIGHWAY ADMINISTRATION. Functional requirements of highway safety features. FHWA-TS-81-216. FHWA. Washington, DC, 1983.

14. US DOT, FEDERAL HIGHWAY ADMINISTRATION. Truck-mounted attenuators. FHWA-TS-88-018. FHWA. Washington, DC, 1988.

15. MINISTERE DE L'URBANISME. Exploitation sous chantier -- mesures d'exploitation du chantier de réfection de l'autoroute A6. Note d'information 16. SETRA. Paris, 1986.

16. AASHTO. Roadside Design Guide. AASHTO. Washington, DC, 1989.

17. TRANSPORTATION RESEARCH BOARD. Glare Screen Guidelines, Synthesis of highway practices No. 66. TRB. Washington, DC, 1979.

18. US DOT, FEDERAL HIGHWAY ADMINISTRATION. Design and operation of work zone traffic control. participants' Notebook. FHWA. Washington, DC, 1987.

19. OECD. ROAD RESEARCH. Road marking and delineation. OECD. Paris, 1975.

20. OECD. ROAD RESEARCH. Roadside obstacles. OECD. Paris, 1975.

Chapter VII

CONCLUSIONS AND RECOMMENDATIONS

VII.1. GENERAL DEVELOPMENTS

The first finding to emerge from assessing the procedures and practices described in the preceding chapters is the large variety of ways traffic is treated at work zones. Member countries have their own cultural and historical identities which affect the specific context in which national road networks and traffic systems have developed; in addition, each site is a special case by virtue of the road at that point, the traffic, the period, the works involved, behavioural and economic imperatives.

However certain common features and developments are apparent. These largely confirm the conclusions which were reached 15 years ago in the first OECD report on this topic (1).

Traffic management has become a major element in planning and carrying out works everywhere. This demands a higher degree of co-ordination and planning than in the past and has given rise to a great many innovations in techniques and equipment. But there are still some important gaps remaining, particularly in our knowledge of what can ultimately be achieved. There is also much still to be done towards improving the cost-effectiveness of safety and traffic control measures.

It is now possible to reverse the general rule of previous decades and state as a basic principle that "the work site should adapt to traffic constraints" rather than vice versa. At the present time this is particularly true on the most heavily trafficked major motorways and is progressively spreading over the whole network as traffic levels and maintenance works increase.

Furthermore, as in other traffic management sectors, greater importance is being attached to driver needs and attitudes. Attention is focusing on decreasing motorists' inconvenience and costs and new means of increasing their awareness and providing them with better and more timely information have been developed. Likewise, the human factors considerations have become more important in regard to the workers when defining activities and safety measures.

VII.2. CONCLUSIONS

Conclusions of this study have been drawn for each topic at the end of individual chapters. The main ones are summarised below.

VII.2.1. Safety

-- Carefully choose the timing of work activities and off peak periods, if possible at daytime, and control of duration;

-- Monitor behaviour and hazards, and adapt signing, guidance and safety devices, particularly for crossovers;

-- Standardize buffer zones and crashworthiness equipment;

-- Keep good visibility and conspicuity in all weather conditions and pay special attention when night works are necessary;

-- Be particularly cautious with short duration or mobile operations;

-- Designate qualified personnel to be responsible for safety and traffic control.

VII.2.2. Evaluation

-- Use national road traffic databases, supplemented by local information, when planning maintenance and traffic management schemes;

-- Optimise use of available resources with cost evaluation methods and predictive models;

-- Work towards a harmonized approach ensuring compatibility between national costing procedures.

VII.2.3. Strategies

-- Specify co-ordination for the technical and financial components right from the start of the planning study and the tendering process;

-- Avoid accumulation of obstructions at the same period or on alternative routes;

-- Prefer shifting or narrowing lanes to suppression or diversion;

-- Enhance workers' training, drivers' information, and permanent monitoring of traffic flow variations.

VII.2.4. Techniques

- -- Select appropriate techniques according to traffic forecast and to work zone geometry or duration of the work zones;

- -- Use standard design such as closure procedure starting with the fast lane, taper length, lane width, access to or merging from the work activity area;

- -- Fix realistic speed limits that could be properly enforced with global work zone appearance or with specific police control.

VII.2.5. Equipment

- -- Check visibility and credibility of signing and guidance, and give drivers enough time to react correctly;

- -- Enhance standard specifications as crashworthiness, easy removal and maintenance;

- -- Provide, adapt and remove appropriate devices for each phase and work zone.

VII.3. RECOMMENDATIONS

Detailed recommendations based on the preceding chapters may be presented under the following headings and summarised in some key words: know, assess, prepare, inform, clarify, adapt.

VII.3.1. Understanding and defining major issues

Developing data bases (traffic, accidents) of a more local and detailed nature, improving the quality of observations of both processes and behaviour so as to better determine the following:

- -- Levels of risk (incidents or accidents);

- -- Levels of inconvenience (delays or congestion);

- -- Levels of dissatisfaction (opinions of inconvenience suffered);

- -- Effectiveness of techniques and devices (at a particular location or with particular equipment).

VII.3.2. Evaluation and planning of operations

Developing methods and models for the following purposes:

- -- Traffic simulation and forecasting (short and long duration);

-- Modeling road capacities and lane restrictions;

-- Evaluating indirect user costs (accidents, delays, inconveniences);

-- Selecting maintenance and repair programmes.

Harmonizing and updating basic values and criteria and adapting them to particular sites.

VII.3.3. Preparing for and co-ordinating actions

-- Integrating safety and traffic control aspects at all stages from project design to the completion of works;

-- Keeping the original number of lanes as long as possible;

-- Co-ordination with other works on the same road or in the same area and selection of a period for works;

-- Worker training and consultation of residents and/or users.

VII.3.4. Monitoring traffic and informing drivers

-- Improving traffic monitoring and the methods for detecting disruptions;

-- Organising rapid intervention and queue protection operations;

-- Using both preliminary and in-car information and testing new modes of communication to warn or advise users about actual difficulties.

VII.3.5. Increasing the credibility and realism of measures

-- Intensifying preliminary studies and systematic checks with a view to:

. Improving driver guidance (visible, continuous traffic guidance systems);

. Simplifying drivers' decisions and manoeuvres (advanced signing, spacing out of difficulties to be encountered);

. Eliminating any measures or techniques which could appear excessive or unsuitable as work progresses (speed limits, etc.);

-- Taking more account of actual driving behaviour and harmonizing measures to avoid unexpected events and unrealistic demands.

VI.3.6. Innovation and modifying existing equipment

-- Increasing tests and experiments on the:

  - Effectiveness of safety systems, breakability, crashworthiness, energy absorption;

  - Ease of placing, removal and repair;

  - Ease of maintenance and adaptability.

-- Stepping up of on-site checks to ascertain suitability to local conditions.

-- Redundancy of complementary devices to produce a wider impact on road users.

VII.4. RESEARCH REQUIREMENTS

-- In computing techniques and aids:

  - To analyse processes and determine lasting criteria;

  - To select strategies and offer assistance to operators.

-- Engineering devices such as road markings, speed control techniques, "following" signs, etc.

-- Methods of training and improving awareness, making use in particular of the interactive potential of video technology;

-- Studies on driver behaviour and reactions.

VII.5. THE NEED FOR HARMONIZATION

VII.5.1. Temporary traffic signs

The mobility of road users involves increased movements across international frontiers. In order to avoid any lack of understanding or incorrect interpretation it is advisable for traffic procedures to be as uniform as possible in neighbouring countries.

The harmonization of traffic control strategies and techniques has already been mentioned. It should concentrate on the representational aspects of temporary traffic signs (e.g. lane changes) and on the colours used for road markings. These issues should be covered when the Vienna Convention is updated.

VII.5.2. Traffic management

Optimising methods and regulations, often depends on long series of experiments which are difficult both to set up and evaluate. Therefore the use of similar criteria and models in collecting and processing traffic and accident data is desirable.

VII.6. TOWARDS AN INTEGRATED APPROACH

The above examples illustrate major trends and developments, particularly as they relate to the economic evaluation and management of traffic.

They also show that most countries are adopting an integrated approach. Interactions between the various aspects, whether regulatory, economic, technical or behavioural naturally lead to this type of approach which increases the cohesion of planning programmes and provides users with clear, coherent traffic management and safety procedures.

REFERENCES

1. OECD. ROAD RESEARCH. Traffic operation at sites of temporary obstruction. OECD. Paris, 1973.

Annex A

OUTLINE OF THE TRAFFIC MODELLING IN QUADRO 2

QUADRO 2 -- QUeues And Delays at ROadworks -- is a computer program developed in the United Kingdom to assess cost effectiveness of maintenance strategies on motorways and on busy sections of the all purpose network.

As explained in Chapter III, the total cost of major road maintenance consists of the direct works cost and user costs. QUADRO 2 estimates these user costs under several headings:

a) Delays (i.e. extra time costs) due to slower running speeds through the works;

b) Delays due to queues which form when normal traffic demand exceeds the capacity of the work site;

c) Delays due to queues which form when an incident -- a breakdown or an accident -- obstructs the site, further reducing the capacity;

d) Changes in vehicle operating costs arising from reduced speeds through the site and in queues;

e) Increases in total accident costs if accident rates increase, or severities change, as a result of the presence of the works;

f) Changes in journey time, operating costs, and accidents to traffic that diverts to other routes in order to avoid queues, and to the existing traffic on those routes.

QUADRO 2 estimates the above costs on the main and diversion routes by calculating time, vehicle operating, and accident costs both with and without the works present.

The vehicle operating costs are calculated using an average speed for all vehicles, but different averages are used for the unobstructed main route, any queue, the site itself, and the alternative route. Vehicle operating costs associated with incidents, however, are excluded. Each direction of travel is modelled separately.

A.1. BASIC TIME PERIODS

QUADRO 2 estimates these costs for an hour, over which the traffic demand is assumed constant. The calculations are repeated for each hour in the day.

Four different day-types may be modelled. The first represents Monday to Thursday, and the other three represent Friday, Saturday, and Sunday. Different patterns of hourly flow will be used for each day-type, either supplied by the user or generated by the program. Days may be omitted if they will not be affected by the works, e.g. weekends. When the costs have been calculated for a week, they are factored up to the duration of the job specified in weeks.

The patterns of hourly flows are supplied by the program, and the actual levels of flow (unless these are input specifically for the period of the works) are generated according to the road type, which is defined by the seasonal variation of traffic flows on the road.

Road Type	Seasonality	Seasonal Coefficient *
Main Urban	Low	0 - 1.05
Inter Urban	Moderate	1.05 - 1.25
Recreational/Inter Urban	High	1.25 +

* The seasonal coefficient is the ratio of short period counts in August and a neutral month, usually May.

QUADRO 2 assumes that the works take place during certain months, and will generate average hourly flow patterns and average levels of flow for these months. This defined period is called the maintenance season.

Road Type	Maintenance Season
Main Urban	May - October
Inter Urban	May - October
Recreational/Inter Urban	May, June, September, October

A.2. THE NETWORK

The QUADRO 2 network (see Figure A.1) consists of:

i) A main route (A - B), with geometry and traffic flows assumed to be uniform along its length. The works site is positioned on the main route. The location, length, and operating characteristics of the site may be specified separately for each direction. The site provides the only capacity restraint in the network.

ii) A diversion route which may be a single actual route, or a combination of several routes, or a representation of possible alternatives provided by the surrounding network. In each case, a major simplifying assumption is made, namely that all diverting traffic follows the route from A to B. In practice some traffic will follow part of the route, other traffic may re-time their trip, or decide not to travel at all. The diversion route is also assumed to have uniform characteristics throughout its length, and real variations must be replaced by representative average values.

Figure A.1 THE BASIC ELEMENTS OF THE NETWORK

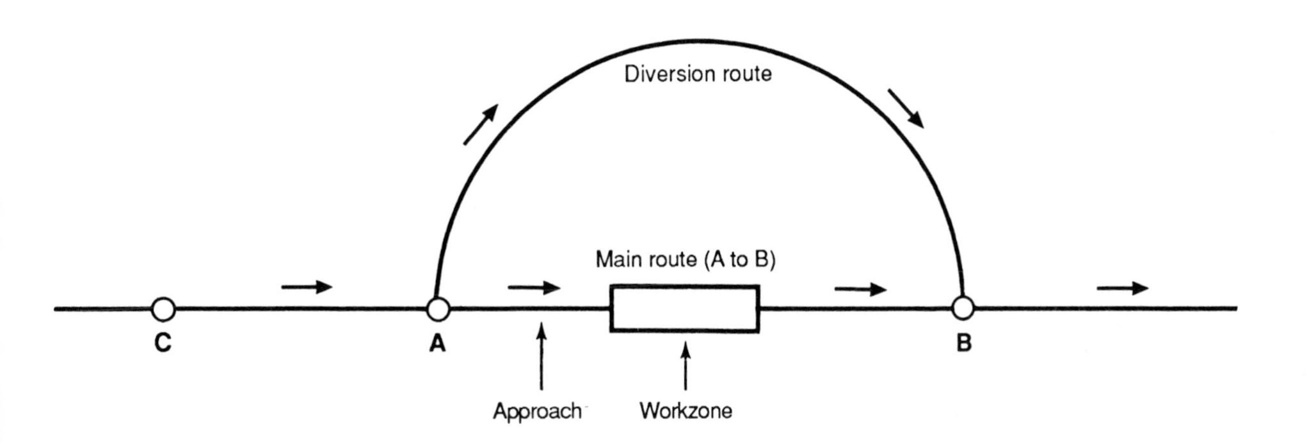

A.3. MODELLING TRAFFIC OPERATION -- WITHOUT QUEUEING

The program initially calculates time, vehicle operating and accident costs on the network with no works present, using a built-in speed/flow relationship for the main route, and a user-specified relationship for the diversion route. The main route speed/flow relationships vary according to the road class and various geometric values input by the user.

The calculations are repeated with the works present. Provided that flows do not exceed the site capacity in any given hour, the only differences will arise from changed speeds in the works section itself. These are calculated using built-in speed/flow relationships selected (as is the site capacity) according to the road class and number of lanes provided through the site.

Costs on the diversion route are unaffected in this case, since there are no changes in flow on the route.

A.4. MODELLING TRAFFIC OPERATION -- WITH QUEUEING

If traffic demand in any hour exceeds the site capacity, a queue will form. QUADRO 2 assumes that below capacity there are no queueing delays.

The queue is assumed to grow until it reaches a certain level (equilibrium queue), after which the excess of the average demand over capacity in that period diverts. The limiting condition at which traffic on the main route will seek an alternative route is:

Journey time via the main route (including any queues and reduced speeds through the site)	=	Journey time via the diversion route

The assumption is that regular drivers become familiar with the delays and that enough of them are willing to divert for this condition to be reached. The program cannot be run without an alternative route, nor with the assumption that people will queue rather than divert.

The user costs are recalculated using the reassigned flows. Account is taken of the reduced speed in the queue, and the fact that diverting traffic will reduce the speed of all traffic on the diversion route, affecting both time and vehicle operating costs.

Queue length is treated deterministically in QUADRO 2 and is a function of demand flow through the work zone and the zone capacity: that is, when demand exceeds capacity a queue will grow; when demand equals capacity a queue will remain constant and when capacity exceeds demand, either there will be no queueing, or a queue will disperse.

The development of a queue within a time period of constant demand and capacity is illustrated in Figure A.2 where it should be noted that the queue development is a function of how many vehicles divert.

The method of determining queue length and the number of vehicles diverting is shown in Figure A.3. Curve A describes the possible variations in the average queue length as a function of the number of diverting vehicles, varying between "nothing diverts" and "everything diverts". Curve A is defined by deterministic queueing theory as described above. Curve E shows the equilibrium queue length as a function of the number of vehicles diverting. The intersection of the two curves determines the amount of traffic diverging and in turn the queue length.

If the queue builds back beyond the start of the diversion route, the characteristics of the affected length of road are assumed to be the same as the main route. If frequent queueing well beyond this point occurs, the user should consider re-specifying the diversion route.

Figure A. 2 QUEUE DEVELOPMENT

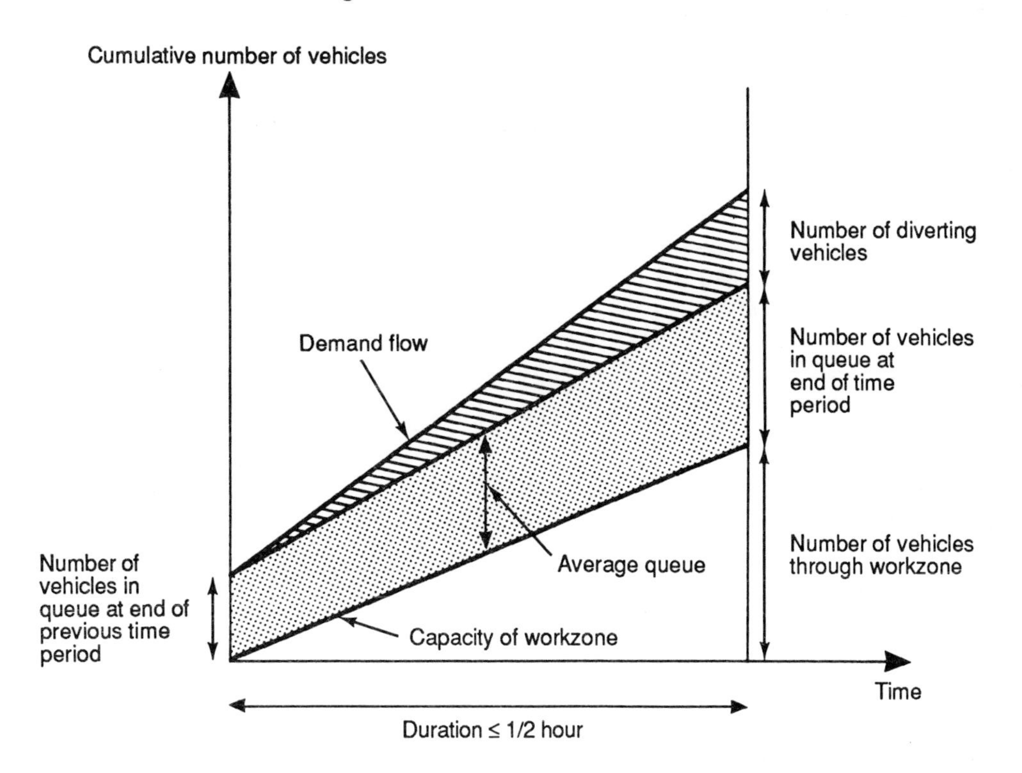

Figure A. 3

DETERMINATION OF QUEUE LENGTH AND NUMBER OF VEHICLES DIVERTING

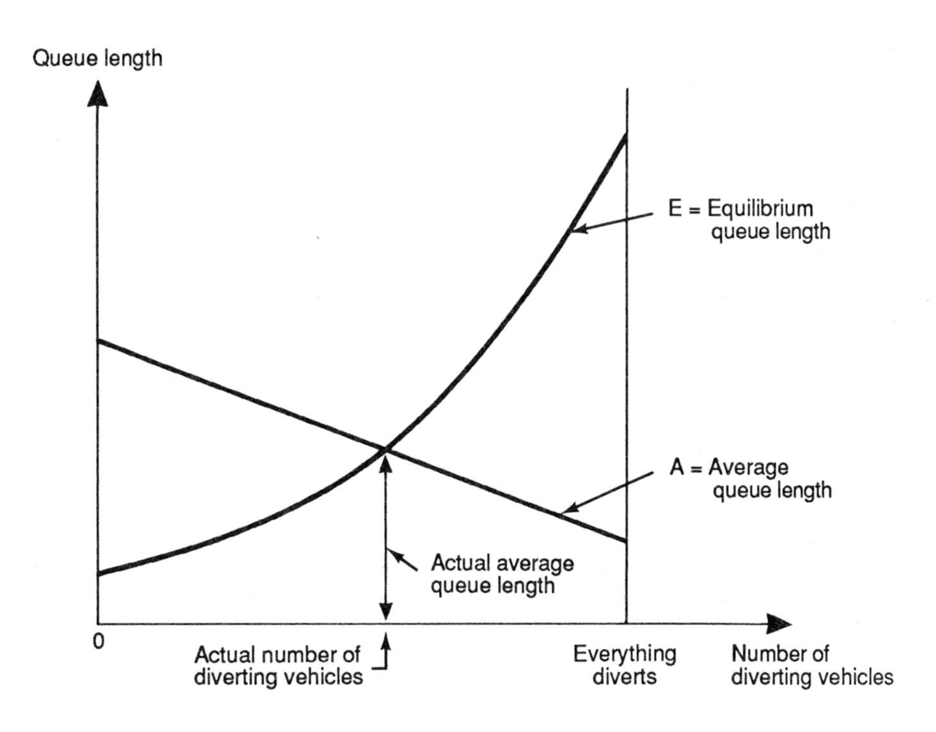

A.5. MODELLING TRAFFIC OPERATION -- INCIDENTS

Incidents occurring in the work zone -- breakdowns and accidents -- will further restrict the capacity and so are likely to cause queueing, particularly at busy periods. The program assumes that an incident blocks one lane totally.

Since incidents are by their nature unexpected, the same queueing and diverting rules, outlined above, cannot sensibly be applied. The program models incidents as occurring at the centre of the work zone and as being of fixed duration. The duration is user-specified and may be different for accidents and breakdowns. No diversion occurs until the queue reaches the point at which the diversion route leaves the main route. As the queue builds further, diversion is assumed to increase linearly until the next upstream junction is reached. At this stage all surplus of demand over capacity is assumed to be diverting.

Once the obstruction is cleared, any queue will be dissipated onto the diversion (according to the above rules) and by the normal discharge through the site. The incident calculations are separate from the "normal" delay calculations, but take account of any queueing already present. The program has built-in rates for breakdown incidents. Average incident durations must be specified, with separate values for breakdowns and accidents. The values chosen will reflect the level of surveillance and availability of recovery facilities at the site.

A.6. MODELLING ACCIDENTS

As outlined in Chapter III, the program uses a "site-presence" accident rate to calculate extra accidents which occur because of the presence of the works -- regardless of length. These accidents are in addition to those calculated on the approach and downstream sections of the main route, using the normal no-works accident rate. A second accident rate, a "site-length" rate, is used to calculate the number of accidents occurring in the site itself. This rate applies over the length of the site and is used instead of the normal no-works accident rate over that length. Empirically based rates are available for motorway roadworks, but, at present, for other works the no-works rates are used.

A.7. DATA REQUIREMENTS

A.7.1. Network data -- main route

The network data consist of length and speed/flow information. The first requirement is to locate points A and B -- the start and end of the diversion route (see Figure A.1). These may be actual junctions if there is a well-defined single route. If several parallel routes are being averaged, A and B may be notional junctions. AB defines the length of the main route and of the diversion route. A and B are not necessarily the closest junctions to the work zone.

For the main route the road class must be known, together with its geometry. This defines the speed/flow relationship, and the number of lanes will affect the physical length of any queue. A suitable accident type must be specified, although the default values can be replaced if local data are available.

Point C is the next upstream junction, used as a queue cut-off in incident delay calculations (see incident modelling, above); the length AC must be specified. Main route geometry is assumed to be uniform throughout CAB. If there are real variations then values relating to the site and approach should be used.

The site is located by the approach length, measured from A to the start of a reduced width section. The program is not normally sensitive to approach length, but if queues are frequently long enough to extend past A, the user should consider whether an appropriate diversion route has been chosen. If both directions are being modelled, two approach lengths and distances AC will be required.

A.7.2. Network data -- diversion route

As with the main route, the diversion route is treated as a single uniform link joining points A and B. QUADRO 2 contains no default information about the diversion route, so the following must be specified explicitly: length, speed/flow relationship, and accident details (i.e. rate, cost). Where the alternative route consists of a number of sections of different characteristics, a separate routine is available to produce a single representative link.

A.7.3. Site data

The user must also supply details of the site length, defined as the length over which the width available to the traffic is reduced. For speed calculations, the program increases this length upstream by 30 m on single carriageways, and by 30 per cent on dual carriageways (subject to a maximum of 600 m), to take account of the reduced speeds in the approaches to work zones.

The type of works layout must be known, e.g. contra-flow with two lanes open. If available, a site capacity can be supplied, which can vary on an hourly basis, otherwise defaults will be used. The data are required for each direction separately. If only one direction is affected, the second direction need not be modelled.

The works duration, in weeks, must be specified. The program assumes that works take place during the maintenance season, defined by the road type specified for the main route. The built-in hourly flow variations available as defaults in the program have been calculated as averages for these maintenance seasons. Thus, if, for example, works during winter months are to be modelled, the defaults should not be used. A works duration cannot exceed 52 weeks.

The direct cost of the works is specified by the user. All cost calculations in the program are at 1979 prices, so a cost-estimate in a different year's price must be converted manually.

A.7.4. Traffic data

The overall proportions of each vehicle category must be specified for a particular year. The categories used are: cars, light freight vehicles, two classes of other freight vehicles, and, finally, buses and coaches.

Different time and operating cost factors are used within the program for each category. The factors for cars assume one-sixth of car travel is on working trips. A local value can be substituted, if available.

The flow classifications are used as a basis for generating hourly variations, throughout the day, in each vehicle class. If classified hourly counts are available, then the percentage of heavy vehicles can be specified on an hourly basis.

The program requires an input of flow level for both the main route and the diversion route. This can be in one of four forms:

-- Annual Average Hourly Traffic (AAHT);

-- 12-hour count in a neutral month;

-- 16-hour count in a neutral month;

-- A 24-hour average flow, representative of the time of year at which the works occur, and of the days to be modelled. This is termed the Maintenance Season Average Daily Traffic (MSADT), and is normally the average over a seven day week.

These flows are two-way totals, and need not relate to the year in which the job takes place. The program contains built-in traffic growth tables for each vehicle category, and low and high economic growth assumptions. These are used to adjust the input flow levels to the year of the job. If local traffic growth figures are available, they should be used in preference to the national default values.

Two other items of information are necessary to enable the program to generate the one-way hourly flows required by the traffic model. The first is the road type, which defines the seasonality of the traffic flow, and hence the average flows during the maintenance season. It also affects the daily variation throughout the week, the hourly variations each day, and the direction splits. The road types, commented earlier, are Inter-Urban (moderate seasonality), Main-Urban (low seasonality) and Recreational/ Inter-Urban (high seasonality).

The second item required is the tidality, which relates the directional split of traffic on the road network. This is particularly important if the site capacity is different in the two directions. A weekday tidality defines the direction of the commuter peaks, whilst a weekend tidality relates to the direction of the weekend tripper peaks (Friday and Sunday evenings).

The hourly flows generated by the program are based on averages of observations at a number of sites. QUADRO 2 is sensitive to flow variations, and site-specific hourly flows should always be used if available. The program can accept one-way or two-way hourly flows in several forms, although it is not possible to mix input and default flow profiles. It is also possible to specify the way in which heavy vehicles divert; for example, the option to retain them on the main route and let only light vehicles use the alternative route.

Annex B

THE TRAFFIC CONTROL PLAN
(In the United States)

B.1. PURPOSE AND USE OF TCP

The objective of the Traffic Control Plan (TCP) is to permit the contractor (tender) to work efficiently and safely while maintaining a safe, smooth flow of traffic.

Traffic control plans show the placement and type of traffic control devices to be used in a work zone as well as information about the type of work zone to be used in each phase of the work.

> "A traffic control plan, in detail appropriate to the complexity of the work project, should be prepared and understood by all responsible parties before the site is occupied. Any changes in the traffic control plan should be approved by an official trained in safe traffic control practices."

A formal Traffic Control Plan (TCP) should be part of all contracts.

The design of TCPs is discussed in the Traffic Control Devices Handbook (1). Materials developed for the TCP may include, but are not limited to:

-- Scaled drawings of the control zone;

-- A list of devices selected for installation;

-- Specifications of special manpower needs, such as flaggers;

-- Copies of permits;

-- Phone numbers of officials to be contacted in an emergency;

-- Scaled drawings of construction stages, including detours;

-- Schedules for times during the day, week, or year when work is not permitted or when certain lanes are to remain open.

Development of the TCP actually starts during the planning process, and specifies the most appropriate work zone type, the phases of work, and scheduling considerations.

The following people and organisations should be involved in the development of a TCP:

-- Transportation officials from local, state and federal agencies including planning, traffic and construction personnel;

-- Police and fire officials;

-- Utility companies.

Also others may be involved depending on the complexity and impact of the project:

-- Business;

-- Residents;

-- Public groups such as Homeowners Association;

-- Local government officials;

-- Contractor-firms tendering for the construction.

B.2. DESIGN OF TCP

The design of the TCP involves consideration of a number of factors (some that were considered in the planning process) to determine the best manner in which traffic can be guided safely through the work zone.

Factors that should be considered in the TCP are the following:

B.2.1. Economic and community

-- Commercial business districts;

-- Residential locations;

-- Recreation areas;

-- Shopping centres;

-- Railroad crossings;

-- Rural areas;

-- Other work planned adjacent to or within the area of the project; and

-- Public information programmes.

B.2.2. Traffic

-- Volumes;

-- Peak hours, including holiday, special event and recreation traffic;

-- Pedestrian traffic;

-- Bicycles;

-- Large vehicles such as trucks and buses;

-- Speed of traffic;

-- Capacity of roadway;

-- Traffic signal operation (effect on existing vehicle detectors);

-- Transit routes and bus stops.

B.2.3. Seasonal changes and weather

These include:

-- Maintaining traffic control during seasonal shutdowns;

-- Loss of visibility and damage to devices during rain or snow;

-- Drainage during heavy rain;

-- Temperature restrictions for some phases of construction; and

-- Maintenance of traffic control devices (cleaning, cutting vegetation away from signs).

B.2.4. Worker provisions

-- Parking of private vehicles;

-- Protection;

-- Flaggers;

-- Access to each part of work area and break area.

B.2.5. Hazards

Hazards created by the work activity within the recovery area such as boulders, drainage basins, pipe, headwalls, blunt ends of guardrail, and sign supports; and

B.2.6. Delays

Delays during traffic control set-up and take-down time (preferably during low traffic volume periods).

B.2.7. Duration

A 24-hour workday may be desirable as it allows the total number of working days to be decreased. Consideration should include:

-- Neighbourhood objection to nighttime noise;

-- Higher cost, for labour and lighting;

-- Higher percentage of drinking drivers at night;

-- Limited availability of services, such as supply of ready-mix concrete or aggregate.

B.3. PLANNING PROCESS

Construction staging determined during the planning process, should be reexamined to determine the complexity of each stage, overlapping of stages, periods of work activities that were overlooked and special problems expected. Areas that must be considered in detail include:

-- The location of work (on roadway, shoulders, or sidewalks);

-- The number of lanes required for the work activity;

-- Hours of a day when a lane may be closed;

-- Whether work may progress simultaneously in both directions of traffic;

-- The length of the work area (controlled staging such as guardrail removal and immediate replacement);

-- Time of exposure to hazards such as dropoff;

-- Time involved, such as curing of pavement of bridge decks.

REFERENCE

1. US DOT, FEDERAL HIGHWAY ADMINISTRATION. Work zone traffic control -- standards and guidelines. FHWA. Washington, DC, 1985

Annex C

ROAD WORK INFORMATION LEAFLET

An example of such information leaflet relating
to the M5 widening in the Midlands, United Kingdom,
is presented on the following two pages.

M5 Widening in the Midlands

When the M5 opened in 1962 it was one of Britain's first generation motorways. The two lane section to the South of Birmingham is now overloaded particularly during the peak hours and at holiday periods or when accidents or essential maintenance work disrupt the flow of traffic. The work that is now going on to widen the motorway is vital. Well over ¼ million drivers use the road every week and I know that they are convinced of the need for improvement.

Work started in 1985 and will continue over the next few years to widen the 13 mile section between Warndon and Lydiate Ash (Junctions 4 and 6) to provide three lanes and a full width hard shoulder in each direction.

The M5, part of a motorway network linking the North-West and West Midlands with South Wales and the South West is one of our essential national economic arteries. Although motorways represent only one per cent of all road mileage they carry 25 per cent of all heavy freight mileage. The M5 is also an important holiday route to the West Country and carries much commuter traffic into and out of the West Midlands conurbation.

During the widening work every effort will be made to minimise delays to motorway users. For much of the time the M5 will still provide the most direct, fastest and safest route.

So while work is under way please check before you travel, stay on the motorway unless directed otherwise by the special signs, observe the mandatory 50 mph speed limit and allow extra time for your journey.

If you are directed onto diversion routes remember those who live, work and play in the area.

Travel safely!

Peter Bottomley

Peter Bottomley
Minister for Roads and Traffic
December 1986

M5 Widening

Lydiate Ash-M42 1988-90
M42-Rashwood Completed 12/86
Rashwood-Warndon 1986-88
Warndon-Strensham 1990 onwards

----- A38 PRIMARY DIVERSION ROUTE
••••• SECONDARY DIVERSION ROUTES

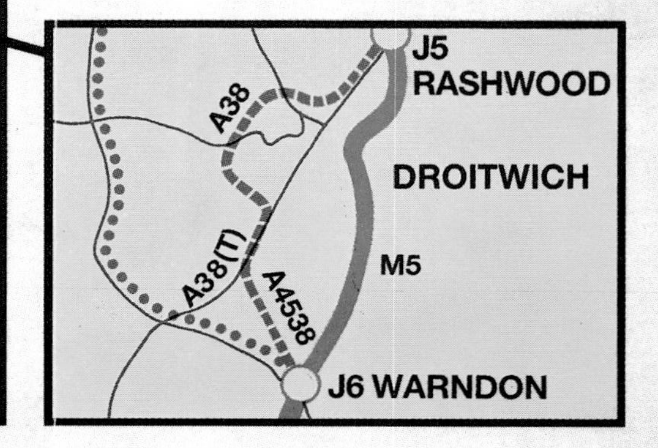

Watch out for special diversion signs on approach to Junctions 3, 4 & 5 from the north and Junction 6 from the south.

During the widening work

Work between junctions 5 and 6 started on the 1st December 1986 and will take two years. Two lanes will be kept open in both directions during the Summer months as well as over the Easter holiday. At other times one carriageway may be reduced to a single lane generally in the southbound direction. The southbound entry slip road at junction 5 and the southbound exit and the northbound entry slip roads at junction 6 may be closed at times.

It will be necessary at times to close the motorway overnight. On other occasions one carriageway only will be closed overnight. These closures are essential for bridge demolition and other work.

What the motorist should do

Planning your journey

1 Allow extra time for your journey – and even more in poor weather. Average delays of 15 minutes may be expected.
2 Try to avoid this part of the M5 on weekdays between 7.30am and 10am and between 3.30pm and 6pm – the most congested times.
3 Use the pre-recorded message for up-to-date information.
4 Tune into the local radio station.

Before you leave

Check tyre pressures, oil, water and fuel and ensure your windscreen washer bottles are full. Check and clean your lights, mirrors, indicators and front and rear screens.

As you go

1 Stay on the motorway unless directed by the special signs to use the diversion routes.
2 Observe the 50mph mandatory speed limit through the roadworks – it is for the safety of both motorway users and construction workers.
3 Drive carefully and keep your distance
 – it's as important in slow traffic as at speed. Don't be distracted – watch the road not the roadworks.
4 If you break down and there is no hard shoulder
 – stop as near to the left of the carriageway as possible
 – stay inside your vehicle and wait for assistance
 – your vehicle will be towed clear of the roadworks free of charge
5 If you break down elsewhere on the motorway
 – stop on the hard shoulder
 – turn on your hazard warning lights and put out a red triangle if you have one
 – use the nearest emergency telephone on your side of the road to alert the police. (Marker posts indicate the nearest phone')
 – Wait for help – do not cross the carriageway or allow passengers to wander onto the road or hard shoulder.
6 If you are directed onto the diversion routes
 – adjust to the altered conditions
 – have regard to residents particularly the elderly and children
 – observe the speed limits

50

Keep in touch

By telephone

A pre-recorded message giving up to date information on closures and diversions during roadworks on the M5 is available 24 hours a day on a special telephone line which is 021 631 2810 .

More general traffic information for a 50 mile radius around Birmingham is available from British Telecom's Traveline service on 021 246 8021.

Information is also available from your motoring organisation.

On the radio

BRMB
(West Midlands) 1152kHz/261m AM: 94.8m FM

Radio WM
(West Midlands) 1458kHz/206m
828kHz/362m AM: 95.6m FM

Beacon Radio
(Wolverhampton & W. Midlands)
990kHz/303m AM: 97.2m FM

Radio Wyvern
(Hereford & Worcester)
1530kHz/196m AM: 96.2m FM

Severn Sound *(Gloucestershire)*
774kHz/388m AM: 95.0m FM

On teletext

The latest road information is available on teletext services:-

BBC Ceefax page 156 **ITV** Oracle pages 184 and 185

Some facts and figures

Widening of the six miles of M5 between junctions 5 and 6 will cost £23 million (1986 prices).

The work will involve altering or rebuilding 10 bridges.

30 acres of land are required for the improvement including landscaping. 6 miles of hedgerow and 40,000 trees and shrubs are to be planted.

Traffic flows

Existing (1984) 44,000 vehicles a day.

Forecast (2010) between 50,000 and 70,000 vehicles a day.

M5

Widening Junctions 5 to 6

Annex D

TRAFFIC MANAGEMENT TECHNIQUES
(1, 2, 3, 4, 5, 6)

Technique (*)

A. Up to 10 m from carriageway there is no need for warning signs, speed reduction or overtaking prohibition. The obstacle (such as bridge falsework) need only to be perceived through a proper delineation.(*)

B. If encroachment of activity area is slight, narrow lanes are the most usual strategy. Only delineation and warning signs are necessary for these lanes, and more seldom also for opposing, standard lanes. Speed control depends on available width, and overtaking prohibition is not normally needed.

Where encroachment gets higher, maintaining total number of lanes needs better use of available width, through use of altered and/or narrow lanes on hard shoulders and/or -- in divided roads -- a contra-flow lane, and even temporarily paved medians or parallel strips. Speed control depends on available width and altered lane geometry. Overtaking prohibition can be envisaged for traffic entering a single lane.

In divided highways, use of hard shoulder opposite to work zone lane is preferable to near shoulder, to avoid leaving work zone as an island in the middle of traffic, and related access problems. For this reason, this strategy is not recommended for 2+1-lane, 4-lane undivided or 2x3-lane divided highways with work zone in the middle lane, F, G or H being preferable. Contra-flow lanes need narrowing and/or use of hard shoulder in the carriageway opposed to work zone, to maintain the number of its lanes.

Temporarily paved medians or parallel strips can be used economically only for short work zones of long duration.

Different situations are summarized in Figure D.1.

(*) Item numbers refer to the techniques listed in Table V.3.

Figure D. 1 TECHNIQUE B

Major encroachment in divided highways: altered and/or narrow lanes plus contra-flow lane (example)

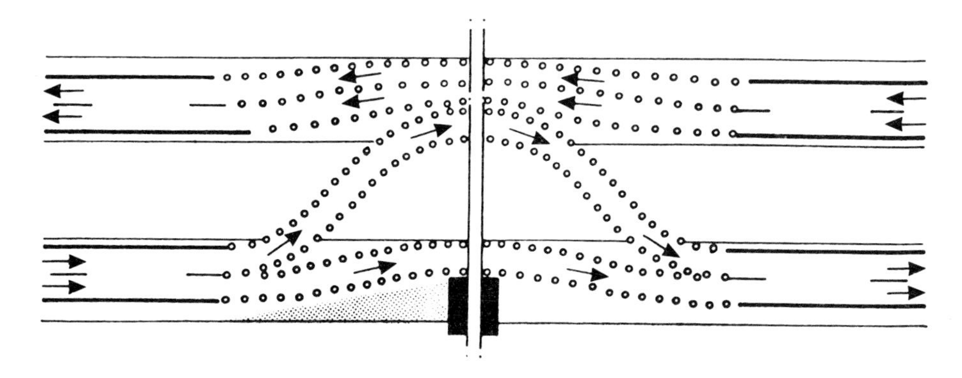

Temporary paving

Median Paving

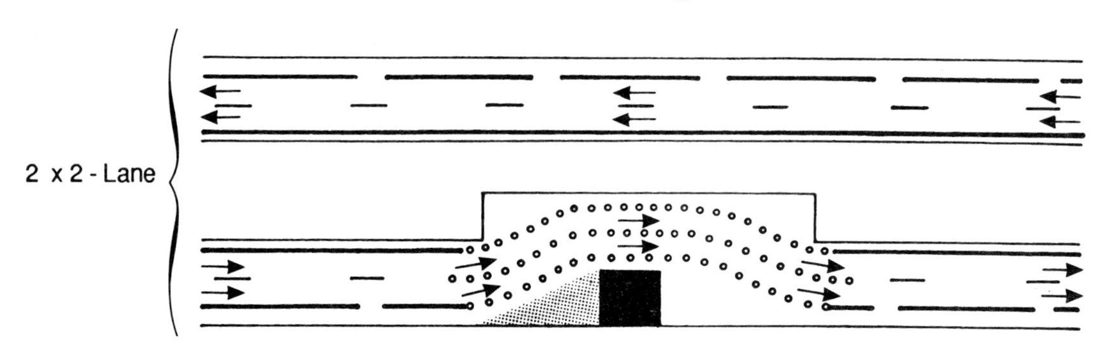

Parallel Strip

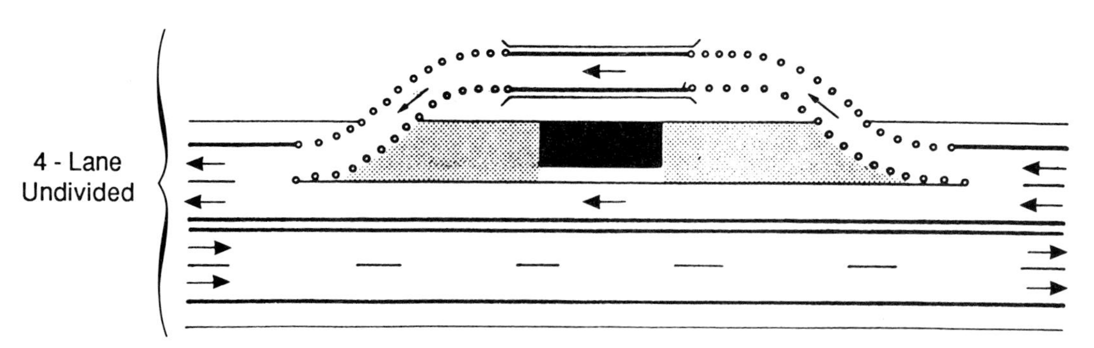

Technique

C. This case is similar to B, except that it can be necessary to close the fast lane temporarily to allow access of equipment and agents to the work zone: then it will be similar to G or H.

D. This case is similar to A or C, according to extent of encroachment. Temporary closure of fast lane may be required for access purposes, and then it will be similar to G or H.

E. In this case it will normally be necessary to use shuttle operation. Warning signs, speed limitation up to complete stop, and overtaking prohibition are needed (Figure D.2).

F. One lane per traffic direction can be maintained, closing one lane and altering the others, with proper delineation and signing. Overtaking prohibition is necessary, and speed limitation cannot usually be avoided. Three situations are possible (Figure D.2):

-- Work zone occupies outer (climbing) lane: preferably fast lane should be first closed then provisionally diverted back to its original position. Opposite lane is not modified;

-- Work zone occupies opposite (descending) lane. Fast climbing lane should be closed in order to allow opposite lane to be temporarily diverted on it;

-- Closure of middle lane only is not advisable because of access problems; in this case it is better to close two lanes, as in E.

G. Where one outer lane is occupied by work zone, allocation of remaining 3 lanes should be made as follows (Figure D.3):

-- If traffic volume is low or balanced, 1 provisional lane to traffic affected by work zone -- closing first the inside lane -- and 2 to opposing traffic;

-- If traffic volume is high and unbalanced, 2 lanes (1 may be contra-flow) should be allotted to direction of higher volume. This may change with time of day or day of week), thus needing reversal of strategy. Problems may arise at divergence of contra-flow lane.

Where one inside lane is occupied by the work zone (Figure D.3) usually only that lane is closed; when traffic is low, both centre lanes of an undivided highway may be closed, facilitating access to work zone and additional lateral buffer zone.

In both cases overtaking prohibition and warning signs are mandatory for traffic direction for which only one lane is left. Speed limitation cannot usually be avoided.

Figure D. 2 TECHNIQUES E and F

Shuttle operation in undivided highways (Technique E)

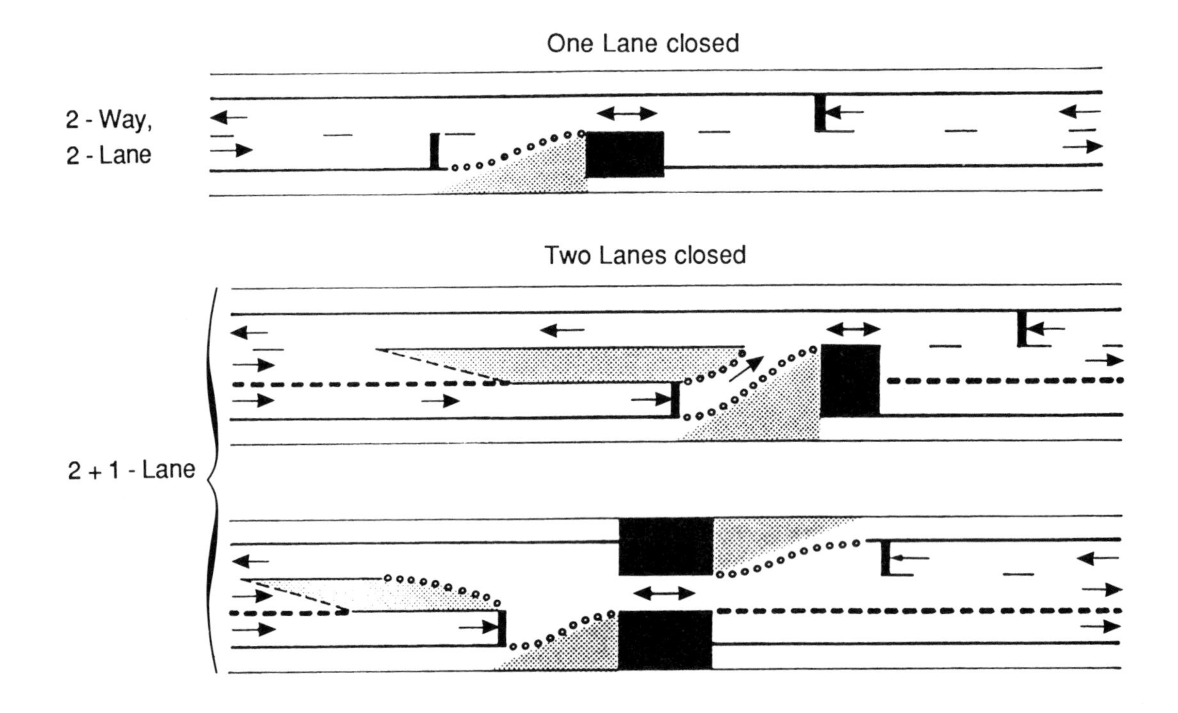

Closure of one lane in undivided highways 2 + 1 - lane (Technique F)

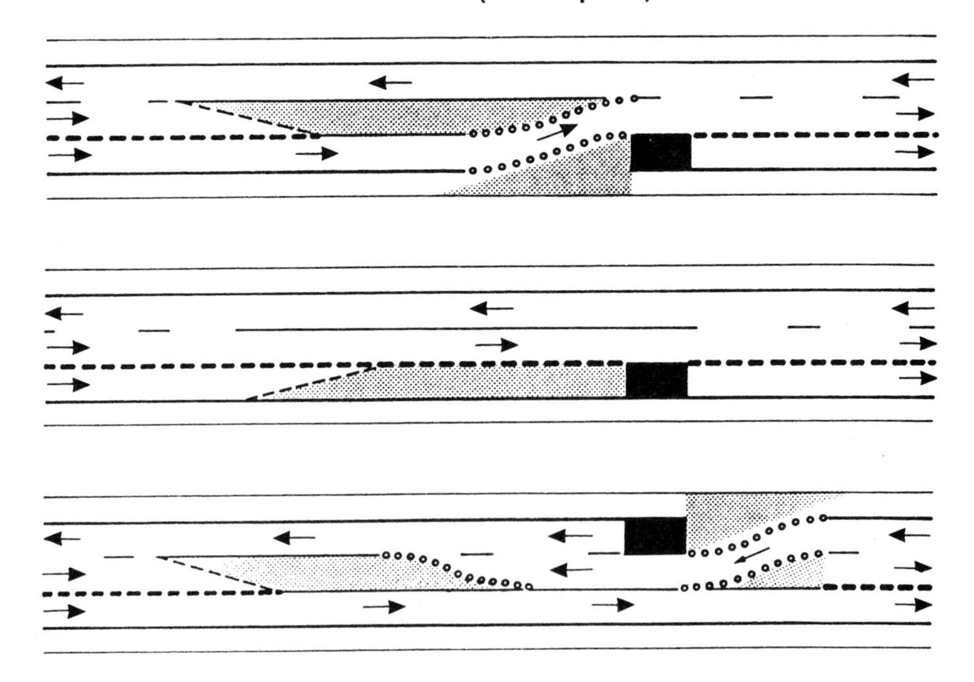

Figure D. 3 TECHNIQUE G

Closure of one outer lane in 4-lane highways

Undivided Highways

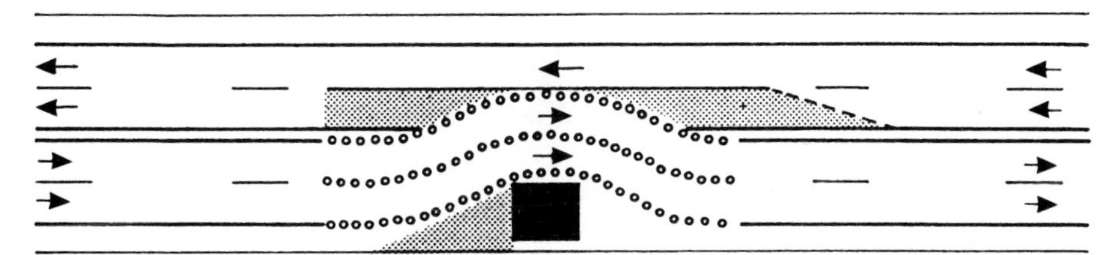

Divided Highways

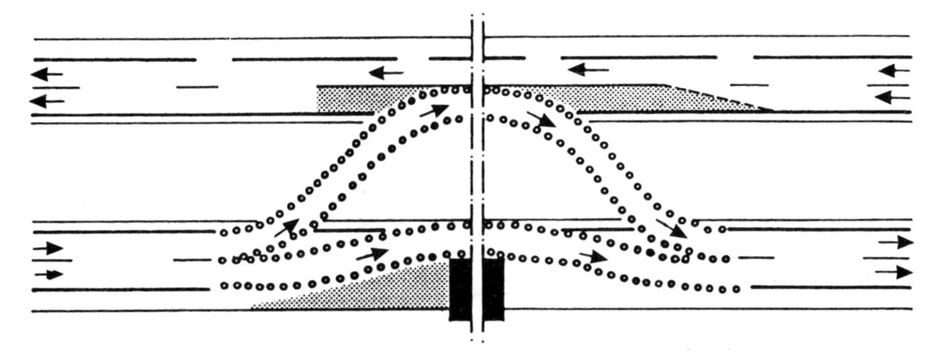

Closure of one inside lane in 4-lane undivided highways

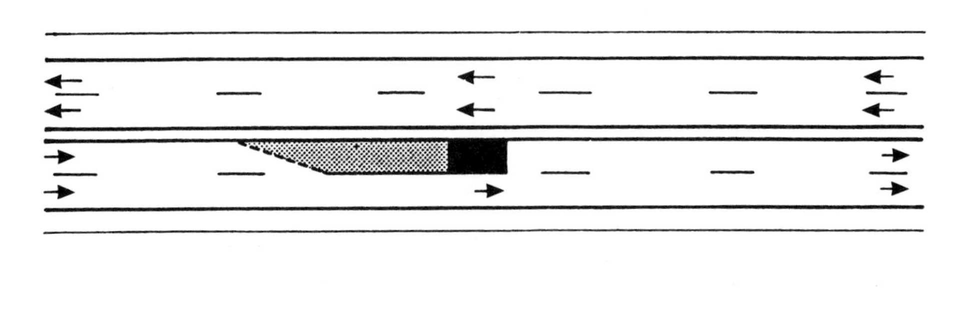

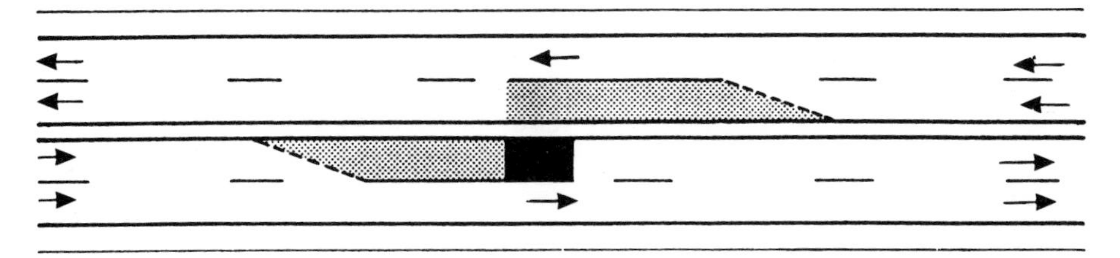

Technique

H. This case is similar to G. Where one lane is occupied by work zone, allocation of remaining 2 lanes for that direction should be made as follows:

-- Normally, fast lane shall be closed, either because affected by work zone or because all traffic is concentrated on the outer lanes before being diverted according to work zone location;

-- If traffic volume is high and unbalanced, and a reduction of number of lanes for traffic direction affected by work zone is not contemplated, even when that means a reduction in the number of those available for the opposite direction, 3 lanes should be allotted to the former; fast lane shall be diverted contra-flow to opposite carriageway (in which fast lane shall have been previously closed), and remaining 2 lanes diverted to inner lanes. This may change with time (f.i. of day or week), thus needing reversal of strategy.

Overtaking prohibition and advance warning signs are mandatory for concerned traffic. Speed limitation cannot usually be avoided.

I. This case is an extrapolation of E, in which opposite shoulder is used. It can be used only in low-volume roads and for short-duration work.

J. Two situations can be contemplated (Figure D.4):

-- Activity area occupies both lanes for one direction: traffic for that direction shall be diverted to a contra-flow single lane in the rest of the carriageway, which will operate as a 2-way, 2-lane facility;

-- Activity area occupies the 2 fast lanes: both fast lanes shall be closed.

Overtaking prohibition and advance warning signs are mandatory for both directions. Speed limitation cannot usually be avoided.

If more than 2 lanes are to be closed, a special study is necessary since it is a bad solution for the high traffic volumes normally associated with 4-lane roads; adaptation to F or M is possible.

K. Where work zone affects either both outer or both inner lanes, situation can be assimilated to G or J.

Where closure of affected carriageway is contemplated, the other carriageway shall be operated as a 2-way, 2-lane facility, with one contra-flow lane. Advance warning, overtaking prohibition and speed limitation are necessary.

Figure D. 4 TECHNIQUES J AND L

Closure of 2 lanes in an undivided, 4 - lane highway (Technique J)

Closure of more than one lane in divided 2 + 3 - lane highways (Technique L)

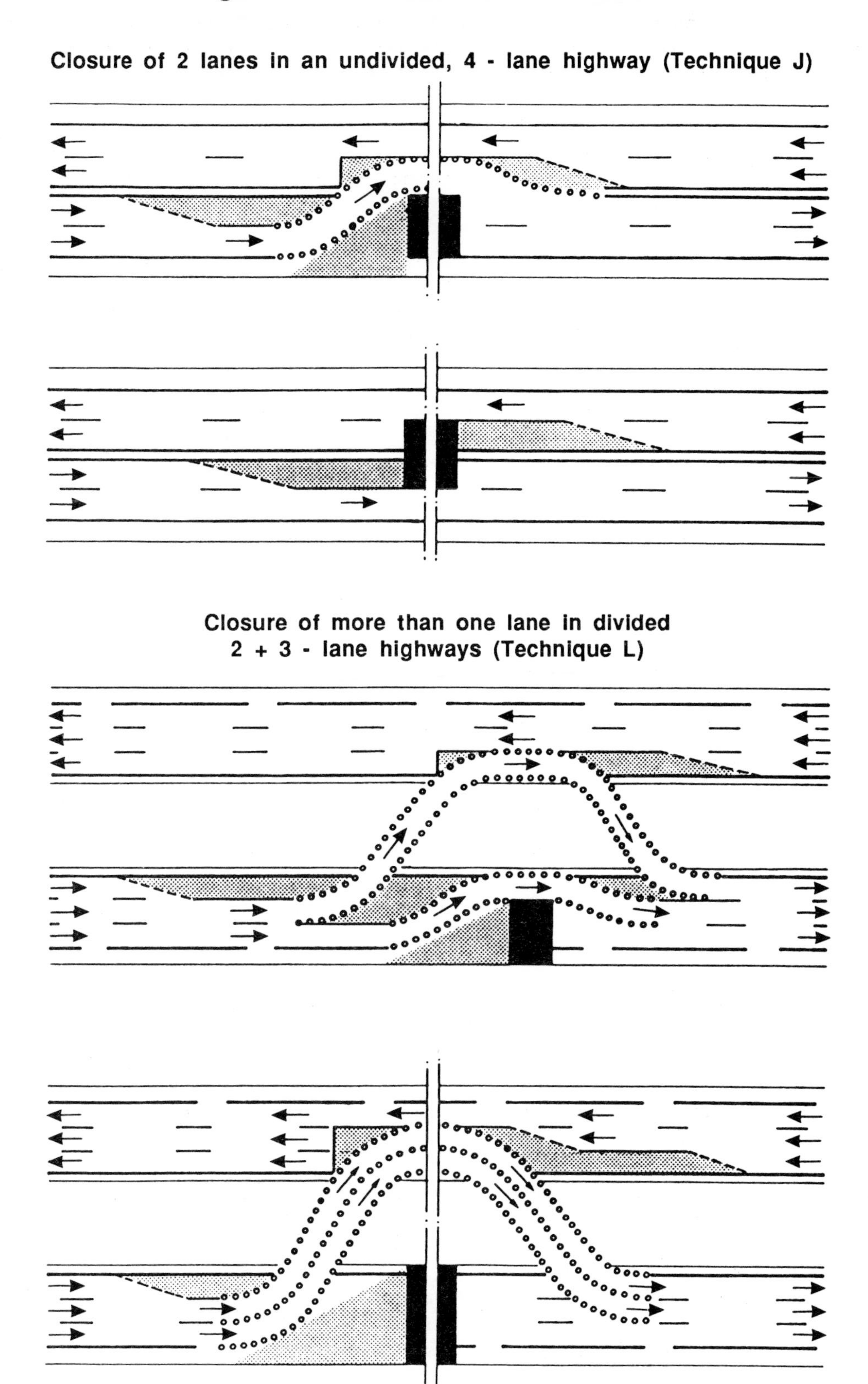

Technique

-- In the affected carriageway only one lane (either outer or inner, but not the middle one) remains open to traffic, and the opposing carriageway is not impaired. This strategy is only possible;

  . For low traffic volumes, which is seldom the case, thus restraining its use to off-peak hours;

  . For very unbalanced traffic volumes (more in the opposing carriageway);

  . In short-duration work for which the traffic management techniques used for mobile operation are deemed inadequate;

-- On the affected carriageway only one lane (either outer or inner, but not the middle one) remains open to traffic, and another lane is carried contra-flow to the opposite carriageway; a strategy similar to H.

  Where full closure of the affected carriageway is necessary, even if this entails a reduction in the number of those available for the opposite direction, two lanes of the former are diverted contra-flow to the inner lanes of the latter (previously closed to opposite traffic): a strategy also similar to H.

In all cases, overtaking prohibition and warning signs are mandatory for concerned traffic. Speed limitation cannot usually be avoided. Traffic demand balance may change with time of day or day of week, thus needing reversal of strategy.

M. Where no detour is possible, this case is also an extrapolation of E in which the undivided carriageway, or one of the divided ones, is blocked and therefore traffic has to come to a complete stop. In divided highways, closure of both carriageways at the same time is hardly possible, due to capacity problems when completely shutting such facilities even for short-duration work; keeping some lanes open to traffic (through a K or L strategy) is always necessary. Multilane carriageways should be reduced to single lane via lane closure to have an orderly stop.

Resumption of traffic can be made through an E situation, if resumption in both directions at the same time is difficult or impossible.

L. Normally, fast lane shall be closed and all traffic concentrated on the outer lanes before being diverted according to work zone location. Three situations can be contemplated (Figure D.4):

REFERENCES

1. DEPARTMENT OF TRANSPORT. Signing for traffic management at certain major road works sites. Departmental Standard TD 14/83. Department of Transport. Roads and Local Transport Directorate. London, 1983.

2. DEPARTMENT OF TRANSPORT. Traffic management of roadworks (other than contra-flow) on the Department's motorways and all-purpose trunk roads. Trunk road management and maintenance notice. Department of Transport. London, 1985.

3. MATHEWS, DH. Traffic management for major roadworks on dual carriageways. Proceedings of PTRC Summer Meeting at Sussex University. Brighton, July, 1984.

4. LARSSON, A. Trafikordningar vid Markeringsarbeter. Vägverket. Borlänge, 1987.

5. BECKER, H and SCHMUCK, A. Verkehrsablauf an Autobahnaustellen - Informationen - Verkehrsplanung und Strassenwesen. Hochschule der Bundeswehr. München, 1983.

6. EMDE, W and HAMESLER, H. Umfallgeschehen an Autobahnbaustellen-Informationen - Verkehrsplanung und Strassenwesen. Hochschule der Bundeswehr. München, 1983.

LIST OF MEMBERS OF THE GROUP

Chairman: Mr. C. Caubet (France)

AUSTRALIA	Mr. J.R. JARVIS Australian Road Research Board P.O. Box 156 NUNAWADING VIC 3131
BELGIUM	Mr. C. LEJEUNE Inspecteur Général des Ponts et Chaussées Division Circulation et Signalisation Administration des Routes Ministère des Travaux Publics W.T.C. Tour n° 3 Boulevard Simon Bolivar 30 1210 BRUSSELS
FRANCE	M. C. CAUBET SETRA 46, avenue Aristide Briand 92223 BAGNEUX
GERMANY	Mr. WEBER Bundesministerium für Verkehr Postfach 200 100 5300 BONN-BAD GODESBERG
IRELAND	Mr. P. McGUINNESS (Corresponding Member) Head Road Traffic Section An Foras Forbartha St. Martin's House Waterloo Road DUBLIN 4
ITALY	Dr. Ing. E. ALBERUCCI ANAS Via Monzambano, 10 00185 ROME
JAPON	Mr. N. MORINAGA Deputy Director National Highway First Division Road Bureau Ministry of Construction 2-1-3 Kasumigaseki CHIYODA-KU Tokyo 100

NETHERLANDS	Ir. A. HOOGVORST Rijkswaterstaat Dienst Verkeerskunde Transportation and Traffic Engineering Division (DVK) P.O. Box 20906 2500 EX's GRAVENHAGE
SPAIN	Mr. J. IZARZUGAZA Servicio de Serguridad Vial Ministerio del Interior Direccion General de Trafico Josefa Valcarel, 28 MADRID 27
	Mr. S. ROCCI Chef del Area de Tecnologia D.G. de Carreteras MOPU R.F. Villaverde, 54 28071 MADRID
SWEDEN	Mr. A. LARSSON Civil Engineer Vägverket, PPt 87 BORLÄNGE
SWITZERLAND	Mr. G. PETERSEN Ing. dipl. EPFZ Office Fédéral des Routes Monbijoustrasse 40 3003 BERNE
UNITED KINGDOM	Mr. M. MARLOW Traffic Operations Division Transport & Road Research Laboratory Old Wokingham Road CROWTHORNE, Berks RG11 6AU
UNITED STATES	Mr. C. BENNETT Director Office of Highway Safety (HHS-1) Federal Highway Administration Department of Transportation 400 7th Street, S.W. WASHINGTON, D.C. 20590
	Mr. R. UMBS Office of Highway Safety, (HHS-12) Federal Highway Administation 400 7th Street, S.W. WASHINGTON, D.C. 20590

IRF	Mr. BERNHARD Fédération Routière Internationale 63, rue de Lausanne 1202 GENEVA
OECD	Mr. B. HORN Mr. C. MORIN Ms. M.D. GORRIGAN

The rapporteurs for the various chapters were: Messrs Weber, C. Lejeune, C. Caubet, S. Rocci, G. Petersen, M. Marlow and R. Umbs.

Members of the Editorial Committee were: Messrs C. Caubet, S. Rocci, G. Petersen, M. Marlow, R. Umbs, M.D. Gorrigan and C. Morin.

Also available

CHALLENGES AND OPPORTUNITIES FOR TOMORROW. 20th Anniversary Seminar (July 1989)
(77 89 02 1) ISBN 92-64-13208-2 180 pages £12.00 US$21.00 FF100.00 DM41.00

ROAD TRAFFIC AND TRANSPORT: TECHNOLOGY, CONTROL AND MANAGEMENT

ROUTE GUIDANCE AND IN-CAR COMMUNICATION SYSTEMS (February 1988)
(77 88 01 1) ISBN 92-64-13046-2 104 pages £8.80 US$16.50 FF75.00 DM32.00

TRANSPORTING HAZARDOUS GOODS BY ROAD (February 1988)
(77 88 03 1) ISBN 92-64-13051-9 146 pages £11.20 US$21.00 FF95.00 DM41.00

DYNAMIC MANAGEMENT OF URBAN AND SUBURBAN ROAD SYSTEMS (April 1987)
(77 87 02 1) ISBN 92-64-12926-X 102 pages £8.00 US$16.00 FF80.00 DM36.00

TECHNICO-ECONOMIC ANALYSIS OF THE ROLE OF ROAD FREIGHT TRANSPORT (July 1985)
(77 86 02 1) ISBN 92-64-12843-3 136 pages £9.00 US$18.00 FF90.00 DM40.00

CO-ORDINATED URBAN TRANSPORT PRICING (October 1985)
(77 85 01 1) ISBN 92-64-12692-9 152 pages £11.00 US$22.00 FF110.00 DM49.00

ENERGY SAVINGS AND ROAD TRAFFIC MANAGEMENT (September 1985)
(77 85 02 1) ISBN 92-64-12753-4 114 pages £8.20 US$16.00 FF82.00 DM36.00

ROAD SAFETY: MEASURES, PROGRAMMES AND GUIDELINES

ROAD ACCIDENTS: ON-SITE INVESTIGATIONS (Fabruary 1988)
(77 88 02 1) ISBN 92-64-13044-6 104 pages £8.80 US$16.50 FF75.00 DM32.00

EFFECTIVENESS OF ROAD SAFETY EDUCATION PROGRAMMES (October 1986)
(77 86 03 1) ISBN 92-64-12881-6 134 pages £7.50 US$15.00 FF75.00 DM33.00

GUIDELINES FOR IMPROVING THE SAFETY OF ELDERLY ROAD USERS
38 pages free on request from the OECD.

OECD ROAD SAFETY RESEARCH: A SYNTHESIS (April 1986)
(77 86 01 1) ISBN 92-64-12814-X 106 pages £6.00 US$12.00 FF60.00 DM27.00

TRAFFIC SAFETY OF ELDERLY ROAD USERS (October 1985)
(77 85 03 1) ISBN 92-64-12756-9 184 pages £7.50 US$15.00 FF75.00 DM33.00

INTEGRATED ROAD SAFETY PROGRAMMES (October 1984)
(77 84 03 1) ISBN 92-64-12620-1 96 pages £5.90 US$12.00 FF59.00 DM26.00

TRAFFIC SAFETY OF CHILDREN (July 1983)
(77 83 02 1) ISBN 92-64-12468-3 110 pages £6.50 US$13.00 FF65.00 DM29.00

ROAD AND BRIDGE INFRASTRUCTURE: DESIGN, CONSTRUCTION AND MAINTENANCE

CURTAILING USAGE OF DE-ICING AGENTS IN WINTER MAINTENANCE (September 1989)
(77 89 04 1) ISBN 92-64-13280-5 128 pages £13.50 US$24.00 FF110.00 DM46.00

DURABILITY OF CONCRETE ROAD BRIDGES (February 1989)
(77 89 01 1) ISBN 92-64-13199-X 148 pages £13.50 US$23.50 FF110.00 DM46.00

HEAVY TRUCKS, CLIMATE AND PAVEMENT DAMAGE (October 1988)
(77 88 04 1) ISBN 92-64-13150-7 176 pages £16.50 US$31.00 FF140.00 DM129.00

TOLL FINANCING AND PRIVATE SECTOR INVOLVEMENT IN ROAD INFRASTRUCTURE DEVELOPMENT (April 1987)
(77 87 03 1) ISBN 92-64-12943-X 150 pages £9.00 US$18.00 FF90.00 DM40.00

PAVEMENT MANAGEMENT SYSTEMS (February 1987)
(77 87 01 1) ISBN 92-64-12907-3 160 pages £8.00 US$16.00 FF80.00 DM36.00

ECONOMIC DESIGN OF LOW TRAFFIC ROADS (November 1986)
(77 86 04 1) ISBN 92-64-12882-4 128 pages £7.50 US$15.00 FF75.00 DM33.00

FULL-SCALE PAVEMENT TESTS (October 1985)
(77 85 04 1) ISBN 92-64-12766-6 102 pages £7.50 US$15.00 FF75.00 DM38.00

ROAD BINDERS AND ENERGY SAVINGS (September 1984)
(77 84 02 1) ISBN 92-64-12601-5 182 pages £8.50 US$17.00 FF85.00 DM38.00

ROAD SURFACE CHARACTERISTICS: THEIR INTERACTION AND THEIR OPTIMISATION (March 1984)
(77 84 01 1) ISBN 92-64-12563-9 206 pages £9.60 US$19.00 FF96.00 DM43.00

IMPACTS OF HEAVY FREIGHT VEHICLES (February 1983)
(77 83 01 1) ISBN 92-64-12423-3 170 pages £8.50 US$17.00 FF85.00 DM42.00

Prices charged at the OECD Bookshop.

THE OECD CATALOGUE OF PUBLICATIONS and supplements will be sent free of charge on request addressed either to OECD Publications Service, 2, rue André-Pascal, 75775 PARIS CEDEX 16, or to the OECD Distributor in your country.

WHERE TO OBTAIN OECD PUBLICATIONS
OÙ OBTENIR LES PUBLICATIONS DE L'OCDE

ARGENTINA – ARGENTINE
Carlos Hirsch S.R.L.,
Galería Guemes, Florida 165, 4° Piso,
1333 Buenos Aires
Tel. 30.7122, 331.1787 y 331.2391
Telegram.: Hirsch-Baires

AUSTRALIA – AUSTRALIE
D.A. Book (Aust.) Pty. Ltd.
11-13 Station Street (P.O. Box 163)
Mitcham, Vic. 3132 Tel. (03) 873 4411
Telex: AA37911 DA BOOK Telefax: (03)873.5679

AUSTRIA – AUTRICHE
OECD Publications and Information Centre,
4 Simrockstrasse,
5300 Bonn (Germany) Tel. (0228) 21.60.45
Telex: 8 86300 Bonn Telefax: (0228)26.11.04
Gerold & Co., Graben 31, Wien 1 Tel. (1)533.50.14

BELGIUM – BELGIQUE
Jean de Lannoy, Avenue du Roi 202
B-1060 Bruxelles Tel. (02) 538.51.69/538.08.41
Telex: 63220

CANADA
Renouf Publishing Company Ltd
1294 Algoma Road, Ottawa, Ont. K1B 3W8
Tel: (613) 741-4333
Telex: 053-4783 Telefax: (613)741.5439
Stores:
61 Sparks St., Ottawa, Ont. K1P 5R1
Tel: (613) 238-8985
211 rue Yonge St., Toronto, Ont. M5B 1M4
Tel: (416) 363-3171
Federal Publications Inc.,
165 University Avenue,
Toronto, ON M5H 3B9 Tel. (416)581-1552
Telefax: (416)581.1743
Les Publications Fédérales
1185 rue de l'Université
Montréal, PQ H3B 1R7 Tel.(514)954.1633
Les Éditions la Liberté Inc.,
3020 Chemin Sainte-Foy,
Sainte-Foy, P.Q. G1X 3V6, Tel. (418)658-3763
Telefax: (418)658.3763

DENMARK – DANEMARK
Munksgaard Export and Subscription Service
35, Nørre Søgade, P.O. Box 212148
DK-1016 København K Tel. (45 1)12.85.70
Telex: 19431 MUNKS DK Telefax: (45 1)12.93.87

FINLAND – FINLANDE
Akateeminen Kirjakauppa,
Keskuskatu 1, P.O. Box 128
00100 Helsinki Tel. (358 0)12141
Telex: 125080 Telefax: (358 0)121.4441

FRANCE
OCDE/OECD
Mail Orders/Commandes par correspondance :
2, rue André-Pascal,
75775 Paris Cedex 16 Tel. (1) 45.24.82.00
Bookshop/Librairie : 33, rue Octave-Feuillet
75016 Paris
Tel. (1) 45.24.81.67 or/ou (1) 45.24.81.81
Telex: 620 160 OCDE Telefax: (33-1)45.24.85.00
Librairie de l'Université,
12*a*, rue Nazareth,
13602 Aix-en-Provence Tel. 42.26.18.08

GERMANY – ALLEMAGNE
OECD Publications and Information Centre,
4 Simrockstrasse,
5300 Bonn Tel. (0228) 21.60.45
Telex: 8 86300 Bonn Telefax: (0228)26.11.04

GREECE – GRÈCE
Librairie Kauffmann,
28, rue du Stade, 105 64 Athens Tel. 322.21.60
Telex: 218187 LIKA Gr

HONG KONG
Government Information Services,
Publications (Sales) Office,
Information Services Department
No. 1, Battery Path, Central
Tel.(5)23.31.91 Telex: 802.61190

ICELAND – ISLANDE
Mál Mog Menning
Laugavegi 18, Pósthólf 392
121 Reykjavik Tel. 15199/24240

INDIA – INDE
Oxford Book and Stationery Co.,
Scindia House,
New Delhi 110001 Tel. 331.5896/5308
Telex: 31 61990 AM IN Telefax: (11) 332.5993
17 Park St., Calcutta 700016 Tel. 240832

INDONESIA – INDONÉSIE
Pdii-Lipi, P.O. Box 3065/JKT.
Jakarta Tel. 583467
Telex: 73 45875

IRELAND – IRLANDE
TDC Publishers - Library Suppliers,
12 North Frederick Street,
Dublin 1 Tel. 744835-749677
Telex: 33530TDCP EI Telefax: 748416

ITALY – ITALIE
Libreria Commissionaria Sansoni,
Via Benedetto Fortini 120/10,
Casella Post. 552
50125 Firenze Tel. (055)645415
Telex: 570466 Telefax: (39.55)641257
Via Bartolini 29, 20155 Milano Tel. 365083
La diffusione delle pubblicazioni OCSE viene assicurata dalle principali librerie ed anche da :
Editrice e Libreria Herder,
Piazza Montecitorio 120, 00186 Roma
Tel. 6794628 Telex: NATEL I 621427
Libreria Hœpli,
Via Hœpli 5, 20121 Milano Tel. 865446
Telex:31.33.95 Telefax: (39.2)805.2886
Libreria Scientifica
Dott. Lucio de Biasio "Aeiou"
Via Meravigli 16, 20123 Milano Tel. 807679
Telefax: 800175

JAPAN – JAPON
OECD Publications and Information Centre,
Landic Akasaka Building, 2-3-4 Akasaka,
Minato-ku, Tokyo 107 Tel. 586.2016
Telefax: (81.3) 584.7929

KOREA – CORÉE
Kyobo Book Centre Co. Ltd.
P.O.Box 1658, Kwang Hwa Moon
Seoul Tel. (REP) 730.78.91
Telefax: 735.0030

MALAYSIA/SINGAPORE – MALAISIE/SINGAPOUR
University of Malaya Co-operative Bookshop Ltd.,
P.O. Box 1127, Jalan Pantai Baru 59100
Kuala Lumpur, Malaysia/Malaisie
Tel. 756.5000/756.5425 Telefax: 757.3661
Information Publications Pte Ltd
Pei-Fu Industrial Building,
24 New Industrial Road No. 02-06
Singapore/Singapour 1953 Tel. 283.1786/283.1798
Telefax: 284.8875

NETHERLANDS – PAYS-BAS
SDU Uitgeverij
Christoffel Plantijnstraat 2
Postbus 20014
2500 EA's-Gravenhage Tel. (070)78.99.11
Voor bestellingen: Tel. (070)78.98.80
Telex: 32486 stdru Telefax: (070)47.63.51

NEW ZEALAND – NOUVELLE-ZÉLANDE
Government Printing Office Bookshops:
Auckland: Retail Bookshop, 25 Rutland Street,
Mail Orders, 85 Beach Road
Private Bag C.P.O.
Hamilton: Retail: Ward Street,
Mail Orders, P.O. Box 857
Wellington: Retail, Mulgrave Street, (Head Office)
Telex: COVPRNT NZ 31370 Telefax: (04)734943
Cubacade World Trade Centre,
Mail Orders, Private Bag
Christchurch: Retail, 159 Hereford Street,
Mail Orders, Private Bag
Dunedin: Retail, Princes Street,
Mail Orders, P.O. Box 1104

NORWAY – NORVÈGE
Narvesen Info Center – NIC,
Bertrand Narvesens vei 2,
P.O.B. 6125 Etterstad, 0602 Oslo 6
Tel. (02)67.83.10/(02)68.40.20
Telex: 79668 NIC N Telefax: (47 2)68.53.47

PAKISTAN
Mirza Book Agency
65 Shahrah Quaid-E-Azam, Lahore 3 Tel. 66839
Telegram: "Knowledge"

PORTUGAL
Livraria Portugal, Rua do Carmo 70-74,
1117 Lisboa Codex Tel. 347.49.82/3/4/5

SINGAPORE/MALAYSIA – SINGAPOUR/MALAISIE
See "Malaysia/Singapore". Voir «Malaisie/Singapour»

SPAIN – ESPAGNE
Mundi-Prensa Libros, S.A.,
Castelló 37, Apartado 1223,
Madrid-28001 Tel. 431.33.99
Telex: 49370 MPLI Telefax: 275.39.98
Libreria Bosch, Ronda Universidad 11,
Barcelona 7 Tel. 317.53.08/317.53.58

SWEDEN – SUÈDE
Fritzes Fackboksföretaget
Box 16356, S 103 27 STH,
Regeringsgatan 12,
DS Stockholm Tel. (08)23.89.00
Telex: 12387 Telefax: (08)20.50.21
Subscription Agency/Abonnements:
Wennergren-Williams AB,
Box 30004, S104 25 Stockholm Tel. (08)54.12.00
Telex: 19937 Telefax: (08)50.82.86

SWITZERLAND – SUISSE
OECD Publications and Information Centre,
4 Simrockstrasse,
5300 Bonn (Germany) Tel. (0228) 21.60.45
Telex: 8 86300 Bonn Telefax: (0228)26.11.04
Librairie Payot,
6 rue Grenus, 1211 Genève 11 Tel. (022)731.89.50
Telex: 28356
Maditec S.A.
Ch. des Palettes 4
1020 – Renens/Lausanne Tel. (021)635.08.65
Telefax: (021)635.07.80
United Nations Bookshop/Librairie des Nations-Unies
Palais des Nations, 1211 – Geneva 10
Tel. (022)734.60.11 (ext. 48.72)
Telex: 289696 (Attn: Sales) Telefax: (022)733.98.79

TAIWAN – FORMOSE
Good Faith Worldwide Int'l Co., Ltd.
9th floor, No. 118, Sec.2, Chung Hsiao E. Road
Taipei Tel. 391.7396/391.7397
Telefax: 394.9176

THAILAND – THAILANDE
Suksit Siam Co., Ltd., 1715 Rama IV Rd.,
Samyam, Bangkok 5 Tel. 2511630

TURKEY – TURQUIE
Kültur Yayinlari Is-Türk Ltd. Sti.
Atatürk Bulvari No. 191/Kat. 21
Kavaklidere/Ankara Tel. 25.07.60
Dolmabahce Cad. No. 29
Besiktas/Istanbul Tel. 160.71.88
Telex: 43482B

UNITED KINGDOM – ROYAUME-UNI
H.M. Stationery Office (01)873-8483
Postal orders only:
P.O.B. 276, London SW8 5DT
Telephone orders: (01) 873-9090, or
Personal callers:
49 High Holborn, London WC1V 6HB
Telex:297138 Telefax: 873.8463
Branches at: Belfast, Birmingham, Bristol, Edinburgh, Manchester

UNITED STATES – ÉTATS-UNIS
OECD Publications and Information Centre,
2001 L Street, N.W., Suite 700,
Washington, D.C. 20036-4095 Tel. (202)785.6323
Telex:440245 WASHINGTON D.C.
Telefax: (202)785.0350

VENEZUELA
Libreria del Este,
Avda F. Miranda 52, Aptdo. 60337,
Edificio Galipan, Caracas 106
Tel. 951.1705/951.2307/951.1297
Telegram: Libreste Caracas

YUGOSLAVIA – YOUGOSLAVIE
Jugoslovenska Knjiga, Knez Mihajlova 2,
P.O.B. 36, Beograd Tel. 621.992
Telex: 12466 jk bgd

Orders and inquiries from countries where Distributors have not yet been appointed should be sent to: OECD, Publications Service, 2, rue André-Pascal, 75775 PARIS CEDEX 16.

Les commandes provenant de pays où l'OCDE n'a pas encore désigné de distributeur devraient être adressées à : OCDE, Service des Publications. 2, rue André-Pascal, 75775 PARIS CEDEX 16.

72547-6-1989

OECD PUBLICATIONS, 2, rue André-Pascal, 75775 PARIS CEDEX 16 - No. 44895 1989
PRINTED IN FRANCE
(77 89 03 1) ISBN 92-64-13281-3